LORRAINE KELLY'S
REAL LIFE
SOLUTIONS

LORRAINE KELLY'S REAL LIFE SOLUTIONS

LORRAINE KELLY

CENTURY

Published by Century in 2003

1 3 5 7 9 10 8 6 4 2

Copyright © Lorraine Kelly 2003

Lorraine Kelly has asserted her right under the Copyright, Designs and Patents Act, 1988
to be identified as the author of this work.

First published in the United Kingdom in 2003 by Century
The Random House Group Limited
20 Vauxhall Bridge Road, London SW1V 2SA

Random House Australia (Pty) Limited
20 Alfred Street, Milsons Point, Sydney,
New South Wales 2061, Australia

Random House New Zealand Limited
18 Poland Road, Glenfield
Auckland 10, New Zealand

Random House South Africa (Pty) Limited
Endulini, 5a Jubilee Road, Parktown 2193, South Africa

The Random House Group Limited Reg. No. 954009

www.randomhouse.co.uk

A CIP catalogue record for this book is available from the British Library

Papers used by Random House are natural, recyclable products made from wood grown in sustainable forests.
The manufacturing processes conform to the environmental regulations of the country of origin

ISBN 1 844 13192 0

Typeset by SX Composing DTP, Rayleigh, Essex
Printed and bound in Great Britain by
Butler & Tanner, Frome, Somerset

To Steve with love

Thanks to Dawn Breslin, Joyce Woodrow, Gay Philips, Nicki Waterman and my mum

contents

Introduction   1

SO YOU AREN'T HAPPY   11

THE BODY BEAUTIFUL   39

DEALING WITH STRESS   91

RELATIONSHIPS   105

LIFE SUPPORT   167

Where to get more help   175

real life

INTRODUCTION

solutions

So you want to be the perfect mother, perfect wife and perfect lover, with the dream job, the body of a goddess, an immaculate home and a couple of perfect children.

Forget it.

No one lives the perfect lifestyle; Kate Winslet is airbrushed, Cameron Diaz has spots and Nicole Kidman has spent hours in the ladies' loo at a glittering première suffering from anxiety attacks.

The very people we idolise and fantasise about often live rather unhappy lives, convinced that everyone else in the world is having a much better time than them. David and Victoria Beckham have made pots of money, but they live in constant fear of their children being snatched by kidnappers, and even Jennifer and Brad have their problems. As Rachel from *Friends*, she might be the poster girl for the shampoo industry, but her poor hubby apparently suffers from snowdrifts of dandruff. It's a minor flaw I know, but I find it strangely comforting.

Most actors I have come across through my work are a seething mass of insecurities

When you look up at that movie screen, where actors make perfectly choreographed love without any mess or squelchy noises and have the most heartbreakingly beautiful faces and perfectly toned bodies, it is all too easy to imagine that their lives are free from everyday hassles, and that they are living a life of utter perfection – but remember, Julia Roberts has a body double for her bum shots and Michelle Pfeiffer thinks she looks like a duck.

In fact, most actors I have come across through my work are a seething mass of insecurities, well aware that they are only as good as their last picture and constantly looking over their shoulder at those younger, sexier, more talented rivals who are snapping at their heels.

They compensate for their fears by demanding the more and more ludicrous 'riders' that appear at the bottom of their contracts.

Why do they do it?

Believe it or not, a lot of it has to do with some of them not actually liking themselves all that much or, to give it the 'proper' terminology, suffering from low self-esteem. Yes, many of these glittering gods and goddesses of the entertainment world are as miserable, insecure and unhappy as the rest of us, and their way of feeling important is to behave like a toddler having a temper tantrum in the supermarket.

I have always maintained that the bigger the entourage a star has in their wake, the bigger the pain in the backside they will be. It never fails and I have seen it time and time again.

Jennifer Lopez, Mariah Carey and Whitney Houston have a cast of thousands following them wherever they go. The wages of these stylists, PR people, make-up artists and general hangers-on are all paid for out of the earnings of the 'star', who is therefore constantly surrounded by people who will never, ever say no because the star is the one signing the pay cheques. This is obviously extremely unhealthy, and the more 'employees' around them there are, the greater the danger the star is distanced from reality.

The bigger the entourage a star has . . . the bigger the pain in the backside they will be

What a lot of these people lack is that one true friend who will be totally honest and tell them they are behaving like a right idiot.

Look at Michael Jackson – clearly no one in his life dares to stand up to him. He undoubtedly had a horrendous childhood, with a father who beat him and told him he was useless and ugly. In fact he really had no childhood at all, which is why at the age of forty-four he has arrested development and has decided to shut out reality and seems to have chosen to revert to being a twelve-year-old boy. Jackson might have incredible talent, and wealth, but despite all of this to me he is one of the saddest people on the planet.

There are of course those who have no need to surround themselves with fawning acolytes in order to have feelings of self-worth.

In stark contrast to the plethora of pop divas and pampered actors, Billy Connolly turned up on his own to our studio to be interviewed, and was as entertaining and hilarious as you would expect.

If you have read his biography – written by his wife Pamela Stephenson, a trained psychotherapist – you'll know that Billy's childhood was also a tough one, and he has spoken openly about being sexually abused by his father. However, he has wrestled with his demons, beaten the booze and come out the other side as one of the happiest and most contented men I have ever met. I am a huge fan, especially as he gives the world what it needs the most – a bloody good belly laugh. For him the glass is always half-full. Yes, it does help that he has an estate in Scotland, a home in LA, a beautiful, feisty, successful wife and bright healthy kids, but he worked hard to earn his money and we shouldn't begrudge him a thing (although I do find it hard to forgive the Lotto ads).

Billy Connolly gives the world what it needs most – a bloody good belly laugh

Emma Bunton is another star with both feet on the ground. She arrived in a black cab along with her mum, and the two of them were friendly, chatty and a complete delight – no need for bodyguards in dark glasses creating a fuss and attracting attention.

Pop Idol Will Young is still a polite, sweet young man who is bright enough to see through all the hype and who could be one of the few 'reality TV' pop acts to have longevity.

A happy, relaxed and secure celebrity doesn't need hordes of minders to make everyone realise how important they are. So, I think the bigger the entourage the bigger the ego – but, deep down, the smaller the self-esteem and confidence.

If you want a screaming example of someone who suffered from low self-esteem, just look at the short life of poor doomed Princess Diana. How many little (and not so little) girls saw her wafting up the aisle in that meringue-like wedding dress and wanted to swop places? She was gorgeous, famous, rich, and she had caught her

Prince. I know it is hard to believe now, but Charles was considered the most eligible bachelor in the world at one time. Diana's role in life was clear. She was our fairytale princess who would live happily ever after. When she gave birth to two healthy sons and then bloomed into a style icon, it looked like she was truly the woman who had it all.

However, in reality she was married to a complex man who was in love with someone else and was exasperated by his young wife's anxieties and insecurities. He must have become somewhat jealous of the public's adoration of Diana, especially when they went on walkabouts together and he was virtually ignored by the crowds.

Diana bloomed into a style icon and looked like she was truly the woman who had it all

As well as her unhappy marriage, her eating disorders and her low opinion of herself, Diana had the unerring ability to pick the wrong kind of man. Her introverted, emotionally inarticulate husband was exactly the person she should never have become entangled with, and then, to escape the unhappiness of her marriage, she threw herself at the likes of James Hewitt, a chinless wonder with the intellect of a stunned bee.

Her death was a horrible shock and hard to accept. I had to report live on the funeral and I spent the night talking with the crowds camping outside Westminster Abbey, waiting to pay their respects. People I spoke to felt sad, angry and bewildered. One woman told me that she felt Diana's death brought home just how precious life is and how we must make the most of our short time in the sun.

What wise words – and what a shame that it is only in times of national tragedy, or when we experience a death or trauma in our own personal lives, that we remember how fleeting life really is.

I am not suggesting for a minute that we should all prance around being shiny happy people twenty-four hours a day – we'd either get locked up or given a well-deserved slap, but we should take some time now and again to re-evaluate our lives and to try and change what we don't like, while squeezing every last drop of pleasure out of things that make us happy.

The first thing to remember is that the solution to most of your problems begins and ends with *you*. There are many things you can do to improve your life – but none of them will happen without real effort and commitment on *your* part.

Sadly, there's no magic pill that will melt away excess flab while eradicating cellulite

Sadly, there's no magic pill that will melt away excess flab while eradicating cellulite, or that will turn your man into a caring sharing paragon who will iron his own shirts. If your boss is a bullying monster, or you have the mother-in-law from hell, nothing you can do will change them from ogres to huggers. However, you can learn ways to deal with them. Often we allow people to treat us badly and we enable them to get away with it, but, if you are unhappy you have taken knocks, believe me it is possible to turn your life around.

Look at Sarah Ferguson. Ten years ago she was the most reviled woman in Britain after paparazzi photographs were printed on the front page of every tabloid showing her frolicking with her lover beside a swimming pool. The infamous 'toe sucking' incident now looks almost innocent when compared with the royal revelations that have surfaced recently. Allegations of male rape, courtiers acting as 'fences' to sell off presents and heirlooms, and accusations of minor royals shamelessly cashing in on their status, make Fergie's exploits seem positively tame. When those photographs were taken, however, Sarah Ferguson was deeply in debt and derided as 'vulgar' by the Queen's inner circle. She was a laughing stock and at an all-time low.

She could simply have lived off her rich relatives and her ex-husband and become part of the useless Eurotrash, comprising the idle rich who spend their days sunbathing on their yachts and their nights in casinos and discos. Instead, Sarah went to the United States, told Oprah she was sorry, and landed herself a couple of big fat sponsorship deals. She worked her bum off (literally, as it happens – one of her major contracts is with a slimming club). Even her harshest critics must now admire what Sarah has achieved. She has an amiable relationship with her rather dull former husband Prince Andrew and her daughters clearly adore her. She also does good solid hands-on work for a children's charity and isn't a mere dabbler like many society women.

I am impressed with Sarah. She is happy to admit her mistakes and she has learned from them.

> *Sarah Ferguson is happy to admit her mistakes and she has learned from them*

Sarah still hasn't been invited to spend Christmas with the in-laws, and has to make do with a turkey dinner for one and an individual Christmas pudding at a cottage on the estate while her ex-husband and daughters play charades with the Queen. However, she has been a staunch supporter of the Royal Family, even when they have treated her with disdain. Despite the snubs and the bad press, Sarah has learned to like herself and she has bounced back to become a real survivor.

Anyone who has gone through pain, suffering, loss and terrible grief, or coped with a physical or mental illness and managed to come out the other side, is a survivor. It might be a young girl who has sorted out her eating disorder, or someone who has overcome a serious illness, or managed to pull themselves up by the boot-straps after being addicted to drugs or booze. The bottom line is that you have to want to change things and you have to be willing to work hard to overcome your problems and to achieve your dreams.

It is safe to say that our expectations as women are far higher now than even ten years ago, and while that's no bad thing – we should be striving for the very best – the problem is that we want it all and we want it RIGHT NOW. In our (doomed) quest for perfection, all too often we don't appreciate what we have. There are too many people who believe that the glass is half-empty, and are so busy rushing around that they never just sit back and savour the moment.

I think many of us have simply lost the ability to enjoy life's little delights

I think many of us have simply lost the ability to enjoy life's little delights. Sometimes there is nothing better than just tidying out your knicker drawer while humming along to Radio 2; or watching re-runs of *ER*, with a big cup of tea and a plate of Hob Nobs; or managing to have a bit of unexpected slap and tickle with your man.

Maybe a lot of people's feelings of discontent are a result of believing too much in American quick-fix solutions and psycho-babble. I am afraid that searching for your inner child is not something I have much time for, and while counselling is extremely useful in certain cases, learning to talk to your nearest and dearest will probably help you just as much if not more.

I don't think we should spend hours on end examining our navels and becoming so self-obsessed that we are in danger of disappearing up our own backsides. However, there's no harm in going somewhere quiet, taking a deep breath, and just thinking about what we want from life. We very rarely take the time to do this.

So, how can you sort out your life and change things for the better?

Well, there are ways you can improve your lot and be happier, healthier and much less stressed.

It is a really good idea to take just a couple of minutes and make a wish list, but it should be a reasonably realistic one, although there's nothing wrong with being ambitious. On my own personal list, I had to cross off being the first woman to walk on the moon and the first to win the World Cup for Scotland by scoring a hat trick against Brazil, but I kept in my ambition to travel to Antarctica and to visit all the states in America, along with my plan to write a best-selling novel. You have to have some dreams.

There are ways you can improve your lot and be happier, healthier and much less stressed

Also write down what you like, and what you don't like, about yourself and about your life. What makes you happy and what do you want to change? I know it might sound a bit daft, but believe me, writing things down concentrates the mind and really makes you think.

Another very simple way of instantly feeling better is to think of something that makes you happy (anything from a whole chocolate orange all to yourself to Mel Gibson's bare bum in *Braveheart*) and just . . . SMILE. It might seem like stating the bleeding obvious, but if you look happier, you will feel happier. Telephone operators are taught to answer calls with a smile on their face, so if you are lucky enough actually to talk to a human being instead of a machine when you are trying to book an airline ticket or get the council to fix the roof, you will know what a difference it makes if you get someone who sounds cheery and helpful. It is well known that we use fewer muscles to smile than to frown – so go for laughter lines instead of the boot-faced look and smile, smile, smile.

Dealing with the problems life throws at us all the time isn't something we are taught at school. No one takes lessons, sits an exam and is then given a qualification in coping with the tough stuff. We are all just trying to muddle through as best we can. Life can be overwhelming sometimes. We can feel like we are running just to stay still . . . so let's find out how we can make the most of our lives and cope with some of the problems that come along the way.

SO YOU AREN'T HAPPY . . .

or How to Like and Respect Yourself

Don't worry, I am not going to ask you to look into a mirror, grin at your reflection and shout over and over again in a loud voice that you adore yourself, you are a wonderful person and the world is a better place with you in it. That kind of behaviour doesn't come naturally to us Brits, and quite frankly the thought of chanting 'I am a goddess' makes me want to giggle and run screaming from the room. However, I do think we can all learn to like and respect ourselves without sounding all phoney and downright daft.

Let's be honest – if you don't like yourself very much and don't rate your abilities all that highly, how can you possibly expect anyone else to think you are worth bothering about?

When we are happy, enjoying our relationships and just generally having a good time, we feel fantastic. Remember how you felt when you first fell in love? The world is a better, brighter place and everything seems wonderful. Work is a joy and you can do no wrong. You are sexy and confident and on top of the world. It's an amazing feeling, but, unless you are very lucky, it doesn't last. However, you can try and get back some of that feeling of sheer unadulterated joy, and the self-confidence that goes along with it.

If you feel happy, it has a profound effect on every single aspect of your life – from your relationships with everyone around you, to your general health and well-being. People will relate positively to your feelings of happiness and self-confidence. It oozes from your pores and crackles like electricity. If you are happy in yourself you reflect that happiness on to others. That's the way it works.

We all know someone who is the life and soul of the party and who actually makes us feel better as soon as they walk into the room. One of my friends is just like that. Davy is a big, tall, red-headed bear of a man who was our best man when Steve and I got married in 1992. He works as a joiner, married with two kids, and for him the glass is always half-full (of lager usually). He is one of those fantastic people who make you smile just by being there.

What's his secret?

Well, he is happy and he can see the funny side of most things. He enjoys life and loves his family very much. They are his whole world. He has been lucky enough to meet his soul mate and he and Maggie are the sort of couple who give singletons hope that one day they too will meet that special person. Davy knew what he wanted in life and he has been lucky enough to get it. He appreciates the value of all he has and lives every day to the full. When he turns up at a party you know that things can really get underway, but he isn't a loud-mouthed attention seeker – he is, quite simply, a great bloke, and very similar in personality to my husband, which is why they get along so well.

On the other side of the coin we all know the office misery guts or the friend or relative who might as well have 'We're all doomed' tattooed across their forehead.

I'm not talking about people who are miserable or unhappy because something awful has happened in their lives and they are in pain; that's a very natural part of dealing with tough times and we have all experienced those. I mean the people who seem to have been born with a scowl on their face and a whinge on their lips, and can see no joy in anything.

Remember how you felt when you first fell in love? The world is a better, brighter place and everything seems wonderful.

These kinds of people are like black holes and they suck the life and energy out of you. They really do bring their own negative atmosphere into a room. They will never see the bright side, and for them the glass is half-empty. Usually their sheer miserableness goes hand in hand with meanness (alongside bigotry this has to be my most hated vice). I am sure you know the kind of person who has short arms and long pockets and for whom every penny is a prisoner. I always find it strange that the meanest people are usually those with plenty of cash – they just don't like spreading it around.

No one minds if our friends and family have to be careful with money if they are feeling the pinch, but being mean just for meanness' sake is unforgivable. Mean people are never ever happy and, unless they do something about it, they never ever will be. They are to be pitied and I'll bet you most of them don't like themselves one little bit.

Low self-esteem

We hear an awful lot about people suffering from low self-esteem. What this really means is that you just don't like yourself very much, and you don't believe that anyone else could possibly find any redeeming qualities about you whatsoever, never mind like or love you.

At its worst, low self-esteem can result in self-hatred and it is the root of many ills and miseries, including eating disorders and depression. It can also manifest itself in monstrous destructive behaviour like bullying and, in extreme cases, physical violence (see Chapter 4).

Here's a classic example of how you can quickly lose your self-esteem.

You are employed in a responsible position at the bank, and you are lucky enough to love your job. It's challenging and the days fly by. You are happy, you are getting a good wage and it's a decent place to work. You have lots of friends there with common interests and – although you might all have a good old whinge about the bosses, the pay, and the conditions – generally you have no real complaints.

Then you hear that the company has merged with another bank and they are downsizing (a ghastly word for a ghastly deed). Out of the blue you are made redundant from a job you thought you had for life. You go out and get plastered with the rest of the gang, and then wake up at 3 a.m. in a panic.

After a restless night you have an enormous hangover and that horrible panicking feeling is getting worse. You feel that you'll never get another job; you feel too old, too over-qualified or too under-qualified and you have lost your confidence.

Now, *you* didn't change one single bit. You are still the same person – but something that you felt defined who you are has gone, and the scary thing is that you had no control over it. Your perception of yourself changes. It is understandable, but it isn't your fault. You are still the same person, but your self-confidence has taken a real knock and you are afraid that people will think less of you. Many people, especially men, become so closely identified with their job that when it's taken away from them, they don't know where to turn. It also happens when people retire and no longer feel that they are worthwhile members of society, making a valuable contribution.

> *It is up to all of us to make sure that we don't become obsessed by our work and that we have a lot more going for us*

There's a lot more to us than the jobs that we do. It is up to all of us to make sure that we don't become obsessed by our work and that we have a lot more going for us in the form of hobbies and interests. If all a merchant banker can talk about is merchant banking, then he quickly becomes a very dull merchant w****r.

Back in 1992, I was working as a presenter with the breakfast station TVam. In those days there was a bizarre kind of lottery where ITV companies all over Britain were asked by the government to bid for the right to broadcast. It was a bit like a silent auction, except you had no idea how much the other bidders had offered. TVam lost out to a new company called Sunrise (which went on to become GMTV) and we were all effectively out of a job.

At that time I had no idea that GMTV would want to sign me up, so I thought my career was over, I would never work again, and that I was about to lose the job of my dreams.

It is horrible when you have no control over what's happening in your life, and I remember feeling as though I had ice in my stomach.

I wrote dozens of letters to producers, went to endless meetings with TV bosses and basically had to 'sell myself' to them, which was something that did not come easy.

I cannot tell you what a relief it was when a couple of months later the bosses at GMTV took me out for a pizza and asked if I would join them. I have been with them ever since, and I honestly believe I have one of the best jobs in the world, but I never lose sight of the fact that it could all end tomorrow.

When a relationship ends, many people go through that phase of thinking they are worthless and hopeless, especially if they are left for someone else. With one in three marriages breaking up, and couples who live together splitting up, there's a lot of pain and anguish out there. It also makes you question your judgement. If you were so easily fooled by them, you wonder 'What else have I got wrong?' It makes you rethink every aspect of your life, and you find your self-esteem and self-confidence being chipped away. The most hurtful thing about your partner having an affair is the lack of trust.

I think I could forgive my husband if he had a daft one-night stand, but a long-term affair, with all the lying, cheating and deceit that goes with it, would break my heart. I don't think I could ever get over that. I would find the fact that he wanted to spend time with, and confide in, another woman a lot more hurtful than the sexual side.

I'll go into this in more depth in Chapter 4 on relationships.

Having a baby can also, perhaps surprisingly, be another confidence underminer. Giving birth is the most amazing thing that will ever happen to you – but like all things that are worthwhile in life, it can be very tough indeed.

It is a huge adjustment when you first become a mum, especially if you have had a demanding job that you enjoyed. There you are at home that first day out of hospital, feeling fat, probably with piles, breasts leaking, and you feel sure that your innards are going to fall out of your front bottom. I looked like I'd been run over by a gritting truck, and still had a huge fat belly weeks after my baby was born. I thought at one point they had made a mistake and left one in there.

I took consolation from Victoria Wood. When she gave birth she suffered from such an enormous haemorrhoid that she phoned her mother and told her despairingly, 'Knit two hats!'

As well as feeling like a blob, you will be overwhelmed by the sheer responsibility of looking after this tiny person who depends on you utterly for absolutely everything. Your world can seem very small when you have a baby, and, unless you are an annoying celeb mum whose figure pings back seconds after giving birth and who walks out of the hospital wearing full slap and a figure-hugging frock, it takes time to lose your baby fat and to adjust to this new way of life. It's normal to feel teary for the first couple of weeks (I remember sobbing at an advert for Heinz soup and being moved by the acting ability of the cast of *Neighbours*, so it shows you what child-birth does to your critical faculties), but if these feelings persist and you are really low then get help as quickly as you can (see page 155 on postnatal depression).

Part of the problem with women losing their confidence after having a baby is down to how they look and feel, but I believe a lot of it is also due to other people's perception of motherhood. I have to bite my tongue when I hear a woman at a party telling everyone she's 'just' a mum and a house-wife and almost apologising for not being a nuclear physicist. Being a mum is the most demanding and certainly the most important job you'll ever do – but instead of being proud of their fantastic achievement, a lot of women can end up losing their self-esteem under a pile of dirty nappies.

I was incredibly lucky to take to motherhood from the first moment I held Rosie in my arms and no one was more surprised than me. I was almost thirty-five when I gave birth and still didn't feel old enough for this huge task. Having a baby is such a 'grown-up' thing to do, and even in my mid-thirties it didn't seem possible that I could be responsible for another tiny little person.

Thankfully I found that Rosie was a fantastically contented baby and, although I was up in the night breast feeding, she usually stopped crying if I sat with her in a rocking chair and lulled her back to sleep.

I do remember that my brain turned to total mush in the first few months and I would put things in the oven instead of the fridge, or walk into a room and completely forget what I was doing there. I would have quite happily sat on my bottom wearing my ratty tartan dressing gown and cuddling my baby for the rest of my

life. However, I had to get back to work and again I was lucky enough to have understanding employers who let me come back gradually. Other women are not so fortunate.

Combining a job with motherhood is a real tough one. It helps to accept that at times you will be racked with guilt, worn out and in need of a helping hand and a sympathetic ear. Don't try and be superwoman – such a being does not exist. Ask for help when you need it and don't try to soldier on. The only way you can do it successfully is to have a really good support system (see Chapter 5 on life support). My husband does more than his fair share around the house and with looking after Rosie, and I have Helen who lives locally and who takes Rosie to school in the morning. (I can pick her up most days, but if I took her to school I would have to leave her at the school gate at 5.30 in the morning, which wouldn't be a caring sort of thing to do.) I also have a good network of school 'mummies' who will help me if I ever get stuck, and there's my own mum (aka supergran) who would walk down from Scotland just to see her granddaughter.

If it all gets too much for you, just remember that Cherie Blair holds down a tough job, is effectively our 'first lady' and has four kids, BUT an indiscreet 'friend' has told us that she is utterly disorganised and frequently stressed out. I think she's a bit like that funny-looking wee duck who glides across the pond, but whose rubbery little legs, out of sight, are going nineteen to the dozen. Remember – even the most outwardly confident people aren't all that secure.

Many people, including myself, have this horrible idea that we will be 'found out'. Just about every person in the public eye I have interviewed is exactly the same. We can't believe we really are good enough, and we think that we have managed to achieve our dream job by sheer luck and bad judgement on the part of the management. I don't think this is anything to worry about and it is rather endearing, but if these feelings start to make you feel terribly insecure and you are forever looking over your shoulder at a possible replacement (either at work or in your relationship), that's when you have crossed the line and it becomes destructive.

How do I start to make things better?

OK. Try this. Write down a description of what you really, truly think about yourself. Be honest.

❑ What do you feel about the way you look?
❑ Are you happy with your weight and your body shape?
❑ Are there bits you would want to change?
❑ How do you rate your intelligence?
❑ Do you think you are a loyal partner, a good lover and a good mother?
❑ What would you change and why?

Now that you are answering some tough questions, how about these:

❑ Do you feel under-appreciated?
❑ Are you bullied at work or do you feel that your bosses and your colleagues just don't recognise your potential?
❑ Does the man in your life expect his meal on the table every night at the same time?
❑ When was the last time he said he loved you?
❑ Do your friends take you for granted?
❑ Are the kids far too cheeky and sassy?

If any or all of the above apply to you then no wonder you aren't all that happy and contented, and could even be bloody miserable. However, the bottom line is that *you* are the one who allows people to treat you badly. This will not change unless *you* do something about it.

You can be too nice for your own good. I don't want you to turn into an über bitch, because then you really will be bitter, twisted and downright miserable, but it is all about putting yourself first for a change and saying 'no' now and again.

You can be too nice for your own good

If you have been going along with being constantly 'put upon' during your relationship or marriage, and have never actually sat down and talked things through, then how will your other half know there's a problem? He *should* realise that you are unhappy, but sometimes people need things spelled out in very large capital letters.

If your boss or supervisor has been getting away with bullying you and treating you badly and you have allowed them to do that, they won't wake up one day and exclaim, 'I have been a prize bitch/bastard to that wonderful employee. I must mend my ways.' *You* are going to have to tell them that their behaviour is just not acceptable, and try and assert yourself.

You have to be prepared for some people not liking your attitude one little bit, but don't let this stop you. You are learning to respect and value yourself and that's worth causing a few emotional ripples among those around you (see page 29). If you have a mate who really only sees you in order to unload all her problems, but never ever listens to you, then you might have to risk her being put out when you tell her the truth. Again it is down to you.

Most women, especially if they have children, put themselves at the bottom of a very long list. I am not saying you should turn into one of the self-obsessed and ghastly 'ladies who lunch' – very few of us living in the real world have the time, money or sheer selfishness to live that sort of life – but I do think that it is very healthy to put yourself first now and again. If you create time for yourself – whether it is just reading a magazine, enjoying a bath or splashing out on a beauty treatment in a salon – what you are doing is saying to yourself: I deserve this time for me. I need to have a bit of a break or a treat and I have earned it. Think like this and you are well on the way to respecting yourself.

Create time for yourself – you deserve it

Remember *Shirley Valentine*? Her life was dull and predictable and she had all her meaningful conversations with the kitchen wall. She and her husband had just stopped talking.

He was the kind of man who expected to be fed steak and chips on a Thursday as soon as he came through the door. When Shirley told him she'd fed the steak to the neighbour's dog, he was dumbfounded and his whole comfy, dull life was threatened. He couldn't cope and flung the chips and egg at her.

Then there was Shirley's daughter who treated the house like a hotel and her mum like a skivvy. Over the years, trapped in a dull marriage, Shirley 'lost' herself.

As we know she escaped to Greece and had a fling with a cute Greek fisherman, but quickly realised that you can't run away from your problems, they come with you. However we must admire her for trying, and sort of succeeding in changing her life.

That movie struck a chord with thousands of women – some of them even fled to Greece to try and find their very own Tom Conti and to drink a glass of wine by the sea shore while watching the sun go down. It is all part of a longing for a change in the dull routine of life and for adventure and for happiness. For some it worked and good luck to them, but, along with your suntan cream and flip flops, you also pack up your problems in your suitcase and you can't leave them behind. There's nothing wrong with desiring a better life – but it is down to you to make it happen. There's no point in being miserable and discontented if you aren't going to do anything to change things so that you feel better about yourself. If you are unhappy with *you* then it doesn't matter whether you are in Cumbria or Umbria, you will still have those feelings of negativity and worthlessness.

So how do you go about changing your life for the better?

Well, you have got to take control of things, you have to be a hell of a lot more positive, and you have to learn to say no and to stand up for yourself.

This is very easy to say, but I do appreciate that it is tough to do – so start off slowly.

Here's an idea. Ask someone who really loves you – husband, boyfriend or best pal – what it is exactly that they think is fantastic about you, and why they think you are so fabulous. If they think you've been at the sherry tell them I said you were to do it.

Write it down (or you will forget).

Are you surprised? Do you feel better about yourself? Do you recognise the person they are describing?

You also have to take time out for yourself. Don't think of it as being selfish, think of it as an essential part of your life and vital for your sense of well-being.

Do something else for me:

❑ Have a think back on your life:
❑ What have been the very best bits?
❑ Was it the first time you were told 'I love you'?
❑ Holding your newborn child in your arms?
❑ Discovering the joys of mini Creme Eggs?

All of us have those moments of magic that we want to put in a box tied with a big, fat red bow, so that we can take them out when we need them. Remembering times in your life when you have been happy will make you feel better, and feeling better is a small but important step towards sorting yourself out.

My magic moments include when I looked at my baby daughter for the first time. I felt this overwhelming sense of love which just washed right over me. I was red faced, sweaty and exhausted and my husband told me I had never looked more beautiful. I actually think he meant it too. If I didn't realise what a prize I had before, I certainly knew it then. I was also amazed to discover that Rosie looked exactly as I had imagined her and how I had dreamed of her. I remember saying, 'Oh it's you', as if I had known her all my life. It was magical and life changing – even with the stitches and the wooziness from the epidural.

I will also never forget the day of my wedding, especially those moments just before I set off in the car with my dad. The house had been in an uproar all morning with everyone laughing, panicking and getting ready. Now in the kitchen there was just me and my dad. I poured him a giant brandy and we had a quiet five minutes to sort ourselves out. He said I looked like a film star. It was absolutely the right thing to say. My dad, who is very shy, also gave the loveliest speech at the wedding. My mum told me afterwards that he couldn't sleep at night for worrying about it and even had my brother video him rehearsing so he would get it just right. It was perfect, straight from the heart and there wasn't a dry eye in the house.

I also experienced a moment of sheer happiness during a break in filming on location in New York. It was a hot day in May and I had had my hair done and had some make-up on and was wearing my favourite jacket and jeans. I actually looked not too bad for a change. I went into Starbucks, ordered a coffee, and was walking down Fifth Avenue when I just thought 'Crikey' – who would ever have imagined a girl from the Gorbals would end up strutting her stuff down Manhattan? I just had to burst out laughing.

It isn't difficult to realise that people pick up on what we think about ourselves, and if we are always putting ourselves down then others will do the same. Remember when poor Diana told everyone that she was 'as thick as a plank'? It was a defensive mechanism because she felt intimidated by the so-called cleverer people around her, but it just made them think smugly that she was a bubble head. She was in fact a very shrewd young woman with an instinctive intelligence that they can't teach you in school, but she gave her detractors ammunition by referring to herself as stupid. Diana thought, 'I may as well say it before anyone else does.'

Putting ourselves down is a trick we often use to disguise our insecurities, but it can backfire horribly and enable people to place us firmly in a type or category which then becomes difficult to escape from.

None of us ever wants to be thought of as a bighead, so, because of that fear, we often go to the other end of the spectrum. You just try and give a British woman a compliment. Tell her you like her dress and she'll call it 'this old thing'; say that her hair looks good and she'll answer, 'I hate it and I am getting it cut.' Tell her that she has lost weight and the response will be, 'Oh I am just wearing clothes that disguise my fat.' We seem to be more at ease taking out the big whip and beating ourselves than giving ourselves a pat on the back.

My friend says that when her husband tells her she looks amazing she just thinks he is after sex. It doesn't enter her head that he might actually be telling the truth because she is without doubt a very fine looking woman. (Mind you, being a typical bloke, probably fifty per cent of the time he actually *is* after sex.)

I know it is difficult when you have been used to thinking in a negative way about yourself, but try and think positively about things you are good at and the skills you have, as well as your good physical features, and you will start to feel a lot more confident. Imagine you are going on a date with George Clooney and you have to list all the things that you think George will find attractive about you – not just your looks, but your personality. Write them down and discover that actually gorgeous George would be rather lucky to have you on his arm.

> *Try and think positively about things you are good at and the skills you have*

How do you learn not to be put upon by everyone? Well, it is simple . . . SAY 'NO'. Saying 'yes' all the time is a bad habit you have gotten into, probably because you want everyone to love you and think that you are such a good girl. You will be amazed that when you do actually say 'no' now and again, people will start to treat you with a bit of respect (once they have picked themselves up off the floor).

Don't think that to become more assertive you have to come over all scary and aggressive. That won't work at all. You will alienate people and ultimately be more unhappy than you were before. What you do have to learn to become is LESS PASSIVE. It is possible to say 'no' without actually saying 'NO'. If your sister asks you to look after her child far too often, or the boss wants you to do overtime yet again, and you are seething because you feel put upon, one way of dealing with it is to offer alternatives.

Tell your sister that you are sorry that day isn't possible for you, but give her the names of alternative babysitters, or do a bit of trading. Tell her you'll look after the baby for a couple of hours if she'll do the same for you. Likewise with your boss. Explain how sorry you are, but offer him a solution. Does someone else want to work overtime? Could things be organised more efficiently, so you don't need to put in so many hours?

What about your elderly mum, dad or in-laws who want you to come round and see them at the weekend, and who make constant and unreasonable demands on you. You maybe see a lot of them but others in the family don't do their fair share. Instead of meekly agreeing like you always do, or becoming aggressive and shouting at them that you are fed up coming over to see them and would rather spend time with your own friends and family, you could deal with it in a way that won't upset you, but also won't create awkwardness. You could say that you can't manage this weekend as you have lots of plans with your friends/family, but you will see if you can get your sister/brother/friend/neighbour to pop in and make sure they are OK. You have been reasonable and you have offered them a solution.

Remember, part of the reason people are clingy and demanding is because you have allowed them to be. It's down to you to change their perceptions of you and what they can get away with. When they see you becoming more assertive people will react in different ways. Initially they might be a bit nonplussed or even annoyed, because they

Remember, part of the reason people are clingy and demanding is because you have allowed them to be

have been used to treating you in a certain way. If you've always been the one at work who makes the tea, brings in the biccies and does all the rubbishy jobs that no one else wants to do, and all of a sudden you say 'no', it may come as a real shock to your workmates. Some of them won't like it one little bit, but they will get over it.

Just remember that you deserve to be respected.

Not realising your full potential

Are you in a job that doesn't challenge you, or a relationship that has gone stale? Do you have friends who you don't actually want to talk to on the phone or even see for a cup of tea, but who you feel 'obliged' to keep in touch with? Well, if you are not dealing with those kinds of people and those kinds of situations in a way that doesn't make your heart sink to your boots, then of course you'll feel frustrated and miserable.

You have to do a bit of a clear out and some reorganisation.

One way of discovering what you really want is to set yourself some goals.

❑ Do you want to lose weight and get healthier?
❑ Do you want to put the zing back into your marriage or relationship?
❑ Do you want to start saving up for that holiday you've always promised yourself?
❑ Do you want to learn a new skill in work, so that you'll get promoted and get a better salary?

It is important to set goals for yourself. Make them realistic, but not too easy. There's nothing wrong with a bit of a challenge.

Most of us work to earn money to be able to afford to feed ourselves and our family. I know

WORK

how lucky I am to have a job that I enjoy, but I also know what it is like to clockwatch and to feel like screaming because only five minutes have gone past since the last time I looked.

I used to work in Bhs on the tights counter during the summer holidays. Being the neat and organised person that I am, I had all the tights in perfect order, both on the counter and in the cupboards underneath. All the American Tan Extra Large were in perfect rows, and the pop socks stood to attention like battalions of highly trained infantry. When I started to growl at customers who would mess up my display, I knew that the job was making me go round the bend, and it was just as well that the holidays ended and I went back to school for my final year, or I might have strangled some poor shopper with a medium pair of 15 denier black stockings.

I was also the second-worst waitress in Glasgow. My best friend Joyce is officially the worst waitress in the city because she managed to trip up and spill the entire contents of a container of parmesan cheese right into my handbag, but I was also utterly hopeless.

The best thing about working in shops and restaurants was that I soon realised I was no good at it. There's absolutely nothing wrong with either job, and a good shop assistant or waitress is worth her weight in gold and deserves at least double the money they earn – but it just wasn't for me.

Sometimes it is as important to know what you don't want as what you do. If you are really miserable in work ask yourself why. Is it too boring, too stressful, do not you get on with your co-workers? What about the boss? Do you feel unappreciated?

Can you change any of the things that make you hate your work? Could you be moved to another department? Is promotion a possibility? Is there anyone you could make friends with?

If your work is really making you miserable then it will affect the rest of your life, and if it is really bad it could even affect your health. You won't sleep well and you'll be stressed out (see Chapter 3 about dealing with stress).

If you can see absolutely no way of changing the things that you hate about your job, and it really is that bad, then maybe it is time to move on. Doing something positive like looking for a new job will make you feel better, but don't leave your old one until you have a cast-iron new position to go to. If you think your work is bad then try being on the dole. It is soul destroying.

RELATIONSHIPS

When you first meet someone and you fall in love, it is amazing, but, as we all know, that feeling of being on a big wheel with your stomach doing somersaults every time you see your 'beloved' doesn't last. You have to work hard at keeping the spark alive.

If you are bored and no longer 'fancy' the person you are with, ask yourself whose fault it is:

- ❏ Are you equally to blame?
- ❏ Do you take each other for granted?
- ❏ Do you irritate and annoy each other most of the time?

The first thing you have to do is talk to one another. I know this sounds obvious, but it is amazing how many couples exist in two separate bubbles and don't actually communicate.

You have to find time to sit and talk quietly and without interruption. You must also stop this from degenerating into an argument: try not to be negative, accusing and aggressive. Some couples use screaming matches to clear the air, but I think that in the heat of the moment you can throw some pretty nasty words at each other and it becomes destructive and hurtful. Think about what you are going to say, be calm, state your piece and then *listen*. Neither of you is a mind reader.

You have to be very clear about what you want from the relationship and what you don't want. Be aware that it might be the case that despite all your efforts, it could be time to move on.

FRIENDSHIPS

Having good friends is one of the best ways of keeping sane and happy (see Chapter 5 on life support). If they really are true mates and love you, then they will always want what is best for you, and they will encourage you in everything you do.

Unfortunately, sometimes friendships can be complicated

and some who call themselves your friend are using you in many different ways that aren't any good for you. We've all experienced the 'friends' who will come and see you, or call you up, and unburden their woes, anxieties and then say, 'That's enough about me, let's talk about *you*! What do *you* think about me?'

Of course there will be times in your life when you'll be the one who needs a shoulder to cry on and vice versa – friendship is a two-way street.

I know it can feel good to be needed, but don't let yourself be taken for granted. It can't be a real friendship if you are the one doing all the running, nurturing and being supportive, if you don't get anything back in return and you aren't being appreciated.

You shouldn't invest too much of your time and energy in a one-way friendship. That's not being selfish, but just having a bit of self-preservation.

What holds you back?

What is stopping you from being happy?

We are all shaped by what happens to us in our childhoods and by the influence (good or bad) of our parents. Often we cannot move forwards because we are trapped in the past.

I know a very unhappy person whose husband left her years ago for another woman. She became very bitter about the split, and to this day still declares that she hates men and will never, ever trust anyone again. She was deeply wounded and suffered a lot of pain, but she has been completely unable to come to terms with something that, sadly, happens to so many couples. She is allowing her former husband still to have influence and control over her life. *She* is the one allowing him still to be able to inflict hurt on her.

He has moved on and, as they had no children together, they virtually have no contact with one another. He has a new family now and probably rarely thinks about his first wife, but she is still that devastated abandoned girl from all those years ago. She has never given herself a chance to meet someone else, fall in love and maybe even have children. For a whole decade she has been like a frozen woman – and she is the only one who is suffering as a result. She has put up barriers between herself and the rest of the world, and by doing so she is very unhappy.

Then there are the women who constantly date the wrong kind of man. Over and over again they pick men who use and abuse them.

I can't tell you how often I have spoken with one of my friends in Scotland as she pours her heart out yet again about how another bastard has taken her for a ride, spent her money and dumped her for someone else. The problem is that she keeps going out with charming rogues who will *always* use and abuse her and leave her with a broken heart. Until she recognises that *she* is the one who can break this habit, and that she has to take control of her life and stop ricocheting from one bad relationship to another, she is doomed to a life of hurt. I think it comes down to the fact that she grew up in the kind of home which was rather cold. Her parents, especially her father, were very controlling and rarely gave her affection and encouragement. I remember how she used to work so hard at school, just to try and get her dad's approval, but no matter how hard she tried it never seemed to be enough.

Her parents are both dead now, but they are still alive in her head. My guess is that she feels she doesn't deserve to be happy and she keeps choosing men who inevitably make her miserable. She might not be aware of it, but there it is.

The past can shape the future and it is hard to break those habits and to escape from them.

A technique that sometimes works – although it is a bit wacky – is physically to 'destroy' something or someone from the past who has hurt you. What you do is take a photograph of the person, or something that reminds you of them, stick it in a pot and burn it. (Please be careful when you do this – I don't want you setting yourself alight.) Or you could just rip it up and fling it in the bin and say, 'That's that. I am done with you and you can no longer hurt me.' I am told that it works and that it makes you feel a whole lot better. It is like drawing a line under that hurtful incident or person and telling yourself that it's time to move along.

You have to believe that you are strong enough, grown-up enough and brave enough to do it. No one is going to come and sort your life out for you. You may find it tough, but, like I keep saying, all the worthwhile things in life are.

What is the worst that can happen?

OK. You are going to make the effort to see that the glass is half-full, and you are going to be a bit more assertive at work and at home. You won't put up with a dull, unfulfilling relationship and you are going to be firm with the friends who don't treat you properly.

The worst that can happen is that the people round about you won't like this new, confident happy person. If they don't that is because they feel threatened, and also because they didn't value you the way they should have.

People who love you and respect you and care for you will be delighted by the new you, so don't be scared. What do you have to lose?

Lorraine's Lifelines

- Instead of automatically saying 'I can't', say 'I'll try'.
- Don't put yourself down.
- Make a list of all your good points.
- Accept compliments gracefully.
- Let the past go – no matter how painful, don't let it sour your life.
- Count your blessings.
- Smile!!! It sounds so simple but it works!!!

REAL LIFE SOLUTIONS

THE BODY BEAUTIFUL

If Marilyn Monroe walked into a Hollywood casting agency today she would be told to get out and lose some weight, especially off her bum and tummy. This is madness, Marilyn was a goddess, but in today's world she would be dismissed as a dumb blonde with a fat ass.

The trend today is to look like you last had a square meal

when you started primary school, and stars of stage, screen and the music charts have turned into lollipop ladies with their big heads and teeny weeny twig-like limbs. Ludicrously, they starve themselves into resembling young boys and then have to go and have breast implants because their boobs have disappeared along with their curves.

I have never seen Renee Zellweger looking more beautiful than when she sashayed into a party dressed as a bunny girl in *Bridget Jones's Diary*. She had the most amazing bosom, gorgeous hourglass figure and shapely legs, but all the way through the film we were told she was fat. For me it spoiled what was otherwise a very good movie, and I am sure I wasn't the only woman sitting there thinking: What is she going on about – she's gorgeous and I would love to have a figure like that. Compare Renee's scrawny body as Roxy in *Chicago* with her appearance in *Bridget* and see what Hollywood has done to women.

> *Now, if you are naturally slim then you are lucky to have been born into a time and place that idealises your shape*

Now, if you are naturally slim then you are lucky to have been born into a time and place that idealises your shape. Forty years ago you would have been told to put some meat on your bones, and 400 years ago, when Rubens was lovingly painting each dimple of his rotund model's cellulite, a very thin woman would have been considered unattractive.

Of course, being grossly overweight isn't at all pleasing to the eye and it is downright unhealthy. When I went on holiday to Disneyland in Florida I could not believe my eyes at some of the morbidly obese people waddling around with bums you could show movies on. Some of them were so fat they could no longer walk on their own two feet and hired electric wheelchairs to get around the parks. The saddest sights were the red-faced, panting children stuffing burgers the size of their heads into their fat faces and chugging it all down with jumbo-sized Coke. Even if some of these kids lost the equivalent in weight of a whole average-sized person, they would still be on the chubby side.

Obesity is an epidemic in the United States and, like most American trends, it has spread over here. A combination of junk food and lack of exercise means that more than a million British children are now severely overweight. It all starts in childhood, and we parents must take the responsibility for passing on bad eating habits to our children when they are toddlers. Carry-out burgers, pizzas, chips, crisps and sweets are full of fat, sugar and salt.

However, let's be realistic; banning them completely isn't really an option for most of us – and anyway, I don't believe it is wise to ban junk food completely, as it will just make it all the more desirable to your children. I can always tell the child who has been brought up on an organic, wheatfree, sugarless diet – he is the one sitting in the corner with his head in the biscuit tin and surrounded by empty KitKat wrappers. Giving your kids sweets and crisps now and again is fine, but we should try and get them to eat as much fresh fruit and vegetables as we can – and we should lead by example.

A combination of junk food and lack of exercise means that more than a million British children are now severely overweight

It is a horrible irony that while we are getting fatter as a nation, eating disorders are on the increase (see page 65 on body image). We *have* to strike a balance so that we look good but we also feel healthy. I think someone who looks like Catherine Zeta Jones is a terrific role model for women because she is curvy, sexy and glowing with good health. You can only look this good by having a proper sensible diet, drinking loads of water and doing some sweaty exercise. Of course the fact that your hubbie is a millionaire and you have the best hair stylists, make-up artists and designers at your disposal also helps, but Catherine was beautiful even before all the Hollywood pampering.

If you are unhappy with your body and want to get in shape, please remember that faddy diets don't work and only end up making you fat and miserable. You can't melt flab away with herbal supplements or pills. Also, although slimming clubs can help you lose weight, they bank on you not being able to keep it off. They rely on you coming back time and time again, handing over your money and then falling off the wagon.

I joined a slimming club just after my daughter was born and I did manage to lose over a stone in a very short time, only to see it all pile right back on again. This was because as soon as I reached my target weight I went right back to my old habits, and I only lost weight in the first place by cheating. Instead of following their food and fitness regime, I would virtually starve myself on the two days before the night of the weigh in. I would also make sure that I took off my watch, rings, earrings and even my knickers and bra when I went to be weighed. I'd wear my lightest shoes with no socks and even take off my necklace and the ratty old scrunchy I use to tie my hair back. Don't tell me you haven't done the same!

As soon as I had been weighed, I would rush off, missing the informative talks which help you to eat sensibly. I was in a real hurry because I had an appointment with a fish supper at the local chip shop. This was my 'reward' for having had no breakfast, lunch or dinner. It was madness. I did lose weight, but of course I was doomed to eventual failure and to feeling tetchy, miserable and unhealthy. It was my own fault that I failed to be a model member of the club. If I had followed their plan to the letter I would have been one of those smiley women in the adverts who can tuck their shirts into their trousers and know the calorific value of everything from an apple to an zucchini.

I know slimming clubs work for some women and I take my hat off to their iron will and sheer determination. If you get an inspirational leader, and maybe go along with a few friends, then you'll have a much better chance of success – but remember that the hard work actually starts when you have reached your target. Keeping the weight off is much more difficult and you will be committed to the slimming club's diet plan for ever and ever.

There are only two ways of becoming slimmer and healthier . . .

1   Eat less rubbish
2   Get up off your bum and do a bit of exercise

It is that simple . . . and that difficult.

Here's an idea, especially if you simply haven't wanted to look at your body and have been wearing jogging bottoms, leggings and skirts with elasticated waists for as long as you can remember.

Strip off and stand in front of a mirror. Please don't worry, there won't be any chanting, but I do want you to take a long hard look at yourself. Bear in mind no one has a perfect body – and a bit of cellulite isn't the end of the world. After all, Jerry Hall might now have an orange-peel bottom but that never stopped her earning a fortune as a model.

So, do you like what you see?

If not, then you are the only person who can do anything about it. Don't put it off until next Monday. Start now.

Remember, there is no quick fix. (Wouldn't it be utterly brilliant if there was though?) Take it slowly and steadily and you will get results. Don't worry if you don't stick to the healthy eating regime and you fall of the wagon now and again. Just don't use that Indian curry blow-out as an excuse to go back to your old ways.

Try eating really healthily during the week – and by healthily I do not mean glowering at a grape; eat proper meals. Then you can treat yourself at the weekend. Remember, this will be an eating plan for life, so you have to be able to stick to it – and if you are on a daft diet you won't be able to live like that for ever. Yes, you will lose weight, but you won't be able to keep it off, and I guarantee you will end up fatter than ever. Being 'on' a diet means that inevitably you will eventually be 'off' that diet and back to your old eating habits. The pounds will pile back on, your clothes will get tight and you will feel utterly miserable. Also, when you are on a diet, especially if it means calorie counting and eating nothing but cabbage soup, eggs or grapefruit, then food becomes the most important thing in your life. It's not healthy and definitely doesn't make you good company. Only a hardened dieter knows the sheer despair of going to bed at night fantasising, not about George Clooney giving you a sponge bath, but about a bowl of low-fat cereal and skimmed milk.

Like so many women, I have struggled with my weight since I was sixteen. I have been on just about every diet there is, and over the years I must have lost the equivalent in poundage of about half a dozen people. Now, I have finally found a plan that works for me and I am sure it could work for you. You won't end up being ultra slim but you will feel healthier, look better and have loads more energy.

It all began back in 1999 when I filmed a fitness video with personal trainer Jenni Rivett. It is the only time I have felt fit and trim and really confident about my body. Jenni was inspirational and she was the one who made me get up off my bum and go for a walk.

I'd 'walk in a fast way' two or three times a week for about forty-five minutes each time, and would go and see Jenni twice a week for a rigorous work-out. I am not a fan of jogging, because it can really damage your knees – and have you ever seen a happy jogger? They all have that pained, constipated look that Bruce Willis does so well in those *Die Hard* films. The great thing about walking is that, once you have bought yourself a decent pair of trainers, it costs you nothing.

I would put on my husband's oldest track-suit, scrape my

hair back into a ponytail, throw on a pair of woolly gloves and plug myself into my mini-radio. The hardest thing was getting out the door, but once I was out walking, I really enjoyed it. I was also eating less rubbish and I really did feel better, with loads more energy.

For three years, I kept the weight off, and then Jenni went back to her native South Africa at the same time as I became pregnant.

It soon became clear that I needed her barking orders at me and *making* me work out properly. I just didn't have the willpower to do it on my own. Sadly, too, I lost the baby, and I turned to comfort eating. I piled on the pounds and became utterly miserable. I used food as a way to numb the pain. So many of us do it. We eat when we are sad and we eat when we are bored. To fight this urge, I used to put on a record, or go and read something. My friend Lyn swears by going off and brushing her teeth whenever she wants a biccie.

Things weren't made any easier by some TV critics having a right pop at my weight gain. Although I do realise they have a job to do, it was very hurtful at the time. I felt very self-conscious, constantly wore black clothes that I could hide behind, and the more unhappy I was, the more I ate. It's a horrible, depressing circle and very difficult to break.

I have since come to terms with the fact that I just wasn't born to be a svelte size ten – and that the latest fashion for showing off your midriff in trousers that are so low-slung they demand a bikini wax just isn't for me – but it takes a long time to learn to accept your body. I think we have to realise that we waste too much time over the years beating ourselves up for not being thin enough. We have to realise that being healthy is what's important and that you have to strike a balance and reach a weight that is right for you – not too fat or too thin, but somewhere in between.

Since the start of the year, I have managed to get back to a reasonable weight through eating properly and getting back out walking. I am now happy being a size 13, even though this size does not officially exist. If I go to Marks and Spencers and Wallis I am a size 12, and if I buy clothes from New Look, George at Asda and Top Shop I'm a 14. Guess where I go to buy stuff when I need cheering up!

I even managed to do the Moonwalk – a 26-mile marathon in aid of breast cancer – which starts at midnight and where women (and a few men) wear highly deco-rated bras and pound the streets of London. It was a very uplifting occasion – not just because of all the Wonderbras, but because there was a real camaraderie. Crossing the finishing line was very emotional and I know I wasn't the only one to burst into tears, especially when remembering friends and families with cancer. I found the experience very humbling as women battling breast cancer walked proudly with their friends, and others walked in memory of loved ones who had died. It was one of those times when you realise how lucky you are just to be alive and reasonably fit and healthy.

I did a fair bit of training for the walk, especially at weekends when, along with my best friend Joyce, we'd go for ten-mile walks which took us all morning and also gave us a chance to have some really good conversations and to catch up with each other properly. I found this a fantastic stress buster, but I was only able to have the time to do it because Steve looked after Rosie for the morning. Of course it is tough to find the time to train for something like the Moonwalk, but as my husband pointed out, I always manage to find the time to sit on my bum and watch *Corrie* four or five times a week. It's about being organised, and I also think having the Moonwalk as a goal made it easier to get over the doorstep and actually walk the walk.

I do take great solace from the fact that even the likes of Oprah can't keep her weight down, despite all her money to buy personal chefs and exercise gurus. She is a wonderfully wise woman and has all that professional help at her fingertips, but she still can't stop yo-yo dieting.

Crash dieting never works and can make you ill. You will lose weight, but you are mostly losing water initially. Then your body starts to feed off itself and you might lose fat, but mostly it will be muscle. Your body then goes into famine mode and reduces your metabolic rate. This means you burn calories slower than before. You will feel dizzy and weak and *starving* hungry. When you do come off the crash diet and go back to the way you were (over)eating before, your body will store as much food as it can in your fat cells, just in case of another 'famine'. Inevitably you will end up fatter than you were before you started.

Crash diets are also boring. You will be ratty, miserable, weak, pasty faced and very probably with breath like a badger's bottom. Yet so many women get locked into this cycle of yo-yo dieting. They are messing up their metabolisms and storing up health problems in the future.

LOSING WEIGHT AND KEEPING IT OFF

If you really are unhappy about your weight, then you know that it is down to *you*. Forget the potions and pills. They don't work and they are a waste of money. Concentrate on eating good, healthy foods and doing a bit of exercise. This is the only combination that will make the weight come off and *stay* off.

I would also advise you not to weigh yourself. You can end up getting obsessed with climbing on and off those damned scales. Muscle weighs more than fat, so, if you are exercising properly, then although you'll look slimmer and more toned, the scales might tell you another story, and that could mean a set back. Instead of using the scales, look out something that you used to love to wear but that no longer fits you and try it on once a fortnight to measure your weight loss.

One of my friends used her wedding dress as her barometer. Ten years and three kids after the wedding she had put on a couple of stones. It took her a year to get the weight off, but when she finally managed to fit into the frock again, she felt fantastic.

A Diet for Life

First of all, make sure you are drinking enough water – very few of us actually do. It is the best possible way to detoxify your body. Tea, coffee, fizzy or diet drinks don't count. Caffeine will give you a false buzz, but then you get the down effect of feeling even more tired, so the more tea and coffee you guzzle, the more the cycle goes on.

Some experts want us to drink two litres of water a day. I have never been able to drink as much as that without spending the best part of the day in the loo – but even if you can drink a litre a day you'll be doing yourself a load of good. There's no doubt that increasing your water intake improves your skin, your hair, your nails and your general all over health.

I wouldn't dream of telling you to give up booze altogether, especially if you enjoy a tipple – but remember, all things in moderation, and binge drinking really does have a terrible effect on your body. If you are at a party, then drink a glass of water for every alcoholic drink.

If you are a smoker you have my sympathy. It is a disgusting anti-social habit and apparently as hard to kick as heroin. If you could only do one thing to improve your health and your life expectancy then quitting smoking would be by far the most effective.

Please don't use smoking as a way of helping you to stay slim. So many young women, in particular, think that smoking is sophisticated and will stop them putting on weight. If you want to use the twisted logic that there isn't much fat on a corpse then keep puffing away – soon you'll be just a bag of bones.

Do not deny yourself anything. If you say you are going to give up all the things you love to eat you will be miserable, unhappy and very dull company. If you desperately want a biscuit, for goodness sake go ahead and have one – just make it a couple of fingers of a KitKat rather than an entire packet.

Get organised and make sure you always have healthy food in the house. If you get hungry between meals, grab a banana. My big downfall is when I come in from work and I am *starving* hungry – I'll often reach for biscuits or chocolate because they are there, instead of making myself some pasta or eating fruit. It's impossible to have just healthy food in the house if you have a family, but you could stop buying as much rubbish and you'll be doing them a power of good as well.

It's important that you recognise when you are most likely to fall off the rails, but don't let food become the centre of your life. Be sensible, have lots of fruit and vegetables around. I cut up lots of carrots, or buy a bag ready chopped and snack on them if I need to eat something.

Be wary of food labels

The Consumers' Association has criticised some manufacturers for using terms like 'Lite', 'No Added Sugar' and 'Low In Fat'. These labels are designed to make food more attractive to people who are trying to eat in a more healthy way.

No added sugar
This sounds very good, but how much sugar is in the product in the first place? Whether it's a chocolate bar, breakfast cereal or a fizzy drink, don't just assume it is healthy and sugar free without checking the label closely.

Reduced fat
There's no legal definition of this. Look carefully at the label. It might be high in sugar which cancels out the 'reduced fat' bit.

90 per cent fat free
Sounds impressive until you realise that the product contains 10 per cent fat – and that's high if you want to cut down your fat intake.

Lite
This is usually a lower-fat version of an old favourite (like spreads, jams, soups). Again check the label. 'Lite' crisps can still contain 22 per cent fat.

To be honest, when it comes to so-called 'slimming foods', I would much rather buy the 'proper' version. The danger of low fat biccies, cup-a-soups and ready meals is that I always need more of them to fill me up, and anyway, I don't think they actually taste as good. I would rather have a proper bowl of soup than a thin diet version, and the danger of low-cal chocolate bars is that you will eat half a dozen of them, which would be the equivalent of a giant Mars Bar.

My mum's chicken soup

This is not only comforting, filling and healthy – it also tastes fantastic, even though I can never get it as good as my mum does. It is a good idea to make a pot on Sunday night and it will last you through the week. It's perfect for lunch; just don't overdo the crusty bread and butter.

You will need:

Two pieces of uncooked chicken
   (legs are best)
Four or five carrots
One small turnip
Four potatoes
One large leek
Four sticks of celery
Parsley

Put the chicken pieces in a pot, cover with water and cook. (Don't use too much water, you can always add more later if you have to.) Chop up the carrots, turnip, potatoes, leek and celery. (Chop up the leek and celery finer than the other chunks, making sure the celery isn't 'stringy'.) Put the veg in the pot with the chicken and water as you cut them up. Cook on a high heat until all the veg is in the pot, then turn it down and let the whole thing simmer for an hour. Add salt and pepper to taste. When the veg is ready (just taste it, you'll know when it is soft enough), take the chicken pieces out and mash the vegetables. Skin the chicken, then chop up the meat and put the pieces back in the pot. Finally, chop up and add the parsley.

This is full of goodness and really filling.

Food is one of life's great joys. Eating out with friends and family is a real treat – don't cut yourself off from all of that. Just remember, all things in moderation. Be sensible, and don't beat yourself up if you do have a bit of a blow-out.

Sarah Dodds came on my show three years ago for a make-over. Her husband had an important work 'do' and Sarah wanted to look her best.

When she went home and looked at the video tape of the programme she was so upset that she broke down in tears. It was nothing to do with the lovely new hairstyle, make-up and outfit we had given her, but for the first time in years Sarah had been forced to take a long hard look at herself and she hated what she saw. She was a size 18 and weighed around sixteen stone. For Sarah, her big TV moment was ruined because she felt fat and ugly.

After watching the tape, she was tempted to dive head first into the biscuit tin, but instead she vowed to change her life and went on a sensible eating plan.

She has been a shining example of how to lose weight properly. It took her three years to lose six stones and slim down to a size 12. She did it the hard way, with a sensible diet and going out walking. In fact, she got so hooked on walking that she and a group of mums from her children's school recently climbed Mount Kilimanjaro to raise money for charity.

I had Sarah back on the show three years after that make-over had given her such a jolt, and she looked fantastic – full of health, vitality and energy, and proof that there really is no easy way to lose weight.

Georgia Taylor, who played Toyah Battersby in *Coronation Street* for five years, shrank before our very eyes as we watched her transform herself from a slightly chubby teenager to a slim confident young woman.

Georgia was sensible. She cut out snacks and 'rubbish' and took up swimming. The weight fell off, and she has found an eating plan and exercise regime that suits her. Georgia admits she felt under pressure to lose weight, but as she is a confident and intelligent woman she did it on her own terms.

Exercise

As well as cutting down on 'rubbish', you really have to do exercise in order to lose weight and to tone up, but it is vital to do something that you actually enjoy.

You don't have to spend money on joining an expensive gym. We've talked about fast walking, and that really is a terrific way to tone up and get your heart rate going. Try and get some friends to go with you – when you are walking and chatting you don't get bored, and you actually get to know each other a whole lot better. Otherwise take a radio or discman. As you tone up you will be getting into all the latest pop tunes or improving your grasp of current affairs. I've actually started listening to Spanish language CDs too. I do get some funny looks as I repeat all the phrases, but it means that I am not only getting a bit fitter, I am learning something valuable as well.

Housework can make you hot, sweaty, tetchy and cross, but I usually put Liberty X on full blast and dance about while I dust, Hoover and tidy up. It makes even the most boring mundane tasks a lot more fun.

Skipping is another good exercise, especially to a really fast pop song.

Don't forget sex. A good old-fashioned bit of nookie gets the heart rate up, especially if you have a decent lover who knows his way around a woman's body and can push the right buttons to get maximum pleasure, fun and fat burning!! Sex is like all kinds of exercise, the more you do it, the more you'll want to do it, and the better it gets.

Although Jenni (my personal trainer) has gone abroad, and I don't get to see her in person, I often work out to the video we did together, just so I can hear her voice encouraging me to do yet another leg lift, arm exercise or sit up – and I get to shout back at her without hurting her feelings. There are loads of good exercise videos in the shops. Get one that suits your level of fitness, push back the sofa, switch on the TV and go for it. They are ideal if you live too far away from the nearest exercise class or don't feel confident or comfortable enough about going to one. You can do your own routine at home and it will take just ten minutes of your time. If you do it every day, I guarantee you will see a difference in a couple of weeks, especially if you combine it with a healthy eating plan. What you want to do is get that metabolic rate up so that you are burning up fat.

QUICK-FIX WORKOUTS
by Nicki Waterman

You don't have to spend hours in the gym every day to get a better-looking body. Experts now say a few lower-intensity workouts throughout the day are just as good for you as one big, hour-long sweat session.

Can You Spare 5 Minutes?

FEEL THE POWER AFTER YOU SHOWER

Want to wake up in a hurry? Crank up the volume on your favourite radio station and rev up your body with some early-morning dancing to at least three songs – if you can stretch to 10 minutes you'll burn at least 50 calories.

EXERCISE WHILE YOU'RE GETTING READY FOR WORK

In the shower do some calf raises (go up on your toes, hold for three seconds, then go down again). This will work your calf muscles and bottom.

Waiting for the bath to fill up, lie on the floor face up with your feet on a chair and do three sets of 12 stomach crunches (put your hands behind your head and curl your head, chest and shoulders towards your thighs using your stomach muscles).

Making tea, do 20 press-ups against the wall.

SQUEEZE YOUR BUM

While waiting for the kettle to boil, squeeze your bottom cheeks together really hard for 10 seconds. Do this five times a day and you'll notice a difference in tone in two weeks. This is because the muscles in the bottom will hold in a semi-flexed position for up to 20 minutes after being worked.

BE A DOMESTIC GODDESS

Housework may be a real chore, but there's an added reason for knuckling down and getting on with it. Vacuuming, ironing, dusting and hanging out the washing can all burn an extra 100 calories. Making the bed; taking off the sheets, turning the mattress, pulling the sheets straight and plumping up pillows and duvets can also burn off at least 50–75 calories. So there's never been a better excuse to keep your house and body in shape!

FORGET CLEANING

Household chores got you tense? Stretch out your upper body using that blasted broomstick. Grasp it behind your back with a wide grip, palms turned behind you. Push it up, as far away from your body as you can. Breathe deeply throughout the stretch. Repeat 3 times. In 5 minutes you'll burn 20 calories.

CLIMB A STAIRWAY TO HEAVEN

On your way to the office, skip the lift. Stairs are a great place to target your thighs and butt, especially if you push from your heels rather than through your toes. Instead of simply walking up, zigzag as you go. Here's how: Push off the inside of your left foot and land softly on the right side of the step with all your weight on your right leg. Now push off the right foot to land softly on your left foot on the left side of the step. Five minutes of vigorous stair climbing will burn 100 calories.

SET THE ALARM

Once you arrive at work set an alarm and get up once an hour to walk around for five minutes. Stretch or do some tummy exercises. By the end of an eight-hour working day, you'll have achieved 40 extra minutes of activity.

AB-TRAINING AT YOUR DESK

Work your abdominal muscles by sitting up straight with your feet on the ground. Breathe in and, on the out breath, pull your belly button and lower abs towards the back of your spine as far as you can. Hold for 10 seconds, breathing at the same time. Do this for 5 minutes, 15 times a day and you'll have strong abs in no time (and these are better than sit-ups).

EXERCISE AT YOUR DESK

To loosen up your neck and upper back muscles, clasp your hands behind your head, then slowly drop your chin to your chest, stretching out your neck muscles. Slowly pull your elbows together, stretching out your upper back muscles.

STAND RATHER THAN SIT

If you have a desk job, do the morning coffee run. Walk over to give colleagues messages rather than use email, it's better still if they're on a different floor. If you're a phone addict, use your time effectively. During a phone call, do lunges (step forward with one leg, drop the knee behind to the floor) and squats (keep both knees directly over the feet and drop your bottom towards the floor), bending your knees to tone your muscles.

WATER COOLER

One little cup of water is but a drop in the bucket of your recommended daily water intake. Gently squat down to refill that cup, keeping your back straight and stomach in as you stick out your butt. To come up, squeeze your butt and abs; then gulp down that cool water. Repeat the move 10 times. So what if your office mates think you're weird? A tight butt is nothing to be ashamed of. Two minutes of gentle squats can burn 10 calories.

PARK BENCH

Before plopping down on a bench to eat your sandwich and watch the world pass you by, seize the opportunity to tone your tummy muscles. A park or street bench is the perfect platform for some simple V-Sit exercises. Sit upright with perfect posture, feet on the floor, chest out and shoulders back. Slowly recline back a few inches while keeping your tummy tight. Hold for 5 seconds and then return to the starting position. Repeat 10 times and burn 5 calories.

HIDE REMOTE CONTROLS

Change TV channels manually. You'll burn off an extra 300 calories a week on average.

SQUEEZE A TENNIS BALL

Do this for two minutes in each hand while you're watching television for an easy forearm and bicep workout.

Can You Spare 10 Minutes?

WALKING YOUR DOG

Taking your dog for a quick walk before and after work will be good for you both and it adds up to an extra 20 minutes of aerobic exercise every day. Walking three to five times a week can also lower your blood pressure by 10 per cent.

SIMPLE RULE

If you can walk there, there's no need to take a cab. If you drive yourself, leave the car on the top floor of the car park and take the stairs.

QUICK TONING EXERCISE

Ten minutes each day is all you need to do this quick toning exercise:

1) March in place for one minute to warm up.

2) Spend two minutes doing lunges to tighten your behind. Step back with one leg and drop that knee to the floor, allowing the front knee to bend.

3) Do squats for one minute. Keeping the knees directly over the feet, drop your bottom towards the floor until your thighs are parallel to the floor. Stand up and repeat.

4) Spend the next two minutes doing regular press-ups. You can rest your knees on the floor if you need to.

5) Follow that with two minutes of abdominal crunches, then spend your final two minutes stretching all of the muscles you've worked.

Can You Spare 15 Minutes?

HAVE SEX IN THE MORNING

Fifteen minutes of morning sex at an active pace is worth 20 minutes of afternoon exercise at the gym because the morning is when the body converts fat stores into energy. Sex also increases the heart rate to about 120 beats a minute, which will help to improve your overall fitness. You can use up to 250 calories per 30-minute session.

GO FOR A WALK — TIP 1

Cancel your morning paper subscription, walk to your local shop before going to work and pick up your daily news in person.

GO FOR A WALK — TIP 2

Jump off the bus a couple of stops earlier and walk the extra distance. You may need to carry your stilettos and change when you get there, but it's worth it. Better still, if you live within an hour's walk to work, why not put on some headphones and walk the whole way? Your metabolism will race for the rest of the day and the pounds will disappear even faster. You can burn up to 400 calories walking briskly for an hour.

WALK IN YOUR LUNCH HOUR

It's your lunch break – get to a park – rain or shine! Take advantage of your lunch hour by walking around the block or park at lunchtime. A quarter of an hour at a fast pace will burn around 100 calories and clear your head at the same time. **Tip:** Whenever possible, have 'walking meetings', taking care of business with co-workers while walking around the block.

SHOPPING TROLLEY

Your friendly neighbourhood supermarket is a good place to circuit-train. Pushing a trolley for half an hour takes care of the aerobic side of the workout. Add toning to your shopping list by squatting for items on lower shelves and doing calf raises to reach the paper towels and other products that are always stashed up high. Every minute that you spend in the supermarket uses up 3.5 calories, so 30 minutes tearing up and down the aisles will burn up just over 100 calories. Don't forget to do some bicep curls when lugging the heavy bags of shopping from the car to the kitchen.

GET GARDENING

Bid adieu to the nine-to-five life with some hoeing, digging, raking or mowing after you get home from work, for 15 minutes burns off 85 calories.

Don't forget to stretch out after doing any exercise, especially when you come back from a walk. It will stop you feeling achey and it feels very, very good.

IF YOU ARE GOING TO START GETTING FIT AFTER NOT DOING ANY EXERCISE FOR A WHILE, PLEASE DO CHECK WITH YOUR GP FIRST.

We live in strange and troubling times where a woman considers she has been 'good', not by being decent and unselfish but because she didn't have a biccie with her mid-morning coffee. Please, please do not put your life on hold by telling yourself that everything will be different when you lose a couple of stones, if you then aren't going to do anything about it. You will just feel miserable. Either try and be happy with the body you have, or make a determined effort to change by doing the following:

- Eat less rubbish.
- Go for a walk.
- Do exercise that is fun.
- Never make food the enemy.
- Eat sensibly during the week and then treat yourself on Saturday and Sunday.
- Don't worry if you have a blow-out – just get back on track the next day. Don't use a binge as an excuse to go back to your old ways.
- Don't be obsessive about diet or exercise.
- Drink lots of water.

BODY IMAGE

A horrible side-effect of the cult of thinness has been the shocking increase in eating disorders. Latest figures show that almost a million people in the UK, mostly young women, suffer from anorexia and/or bulimia.

The worst thing about eating disorders is that they happen behind closed doors. There's so much shame and embarrassment associated with these conditions that it takes a lot longer than it should to get proper help. Thanks to Princess Diana speaking out about her battle with bulimia, and the likes of actress Tracy Shaw talking openly about her anorexia, we now understand a lot more about these conditions and the kind of devastating effect they have on the sufferer and the family.

Anorexia

In parts of the world where being thin is not considered to be either fashionable or healthy, very few people suffer from eating disorders. In the West, however, where thinness is not only acceptable but downright desirable, the number of people with eating disorders is high and growing at an alarming rate. When you look at jobs like fashion modelling, dancing and acting, then the numbers go off the scale.

Anorexia is a horrible illness, both for the sufferer and for those anxious people around them who want to help, but are frustrated and bewildered to see someone single mindedly starving themselves. It usually affects teenagers, but it can begin earlier in childhood. Sufferers are usually young women, but an increasing number of young men are now anorexic. All of them are very clever about disguising how little food they eat.

They begin to diet, see the weight coming off, and feel a

sense of achievement. It is the one part of their lives that they have control over and that can be a highly addictive drug, especially to someone who feels that the rest of their life is outside their control.

One of the side effects of anorexia in young women is that periods stop and puberty can be 'put off'. For those who simply don't feel ready for the responsibility of growing up, this is their way of not having to deal with it.

I received a letter from a mother with a six-year-old girl who was suffering from anorexia. This beautiful child was being bullied at school for being 'fat', and was refusing to eat. She'd pretend to eat, but hide the food, and her mother was at the end of her tether. Luckily the girl was able to get good counselling and is making a recovery, but it really brought home to me the kinds of pressures even very young children are under to conform to a certain body type.

Anorexia can also be triggered off by a trauma, perhaps a death in the family. It can also start with a desire to be thin like those models in the magazines, or because of a burning ambition to be a dancer. It begins with dieting and it can end in appalling health problems or even death.

Sufferers all have an unhealthy relationship with food, and will often cook meals for the whole family, but eat nothing themselves. Food becomes the most important thing in their lives and it is also the enemy.

There's no such thing as a 'typical' anorexic, but many are bright, high achievers with parents who push them to do well – but that is not always the case.

Tracy Shaw is one of the country's best known former

sufferers. Tracy is well known for playing Maxine in *Coronation Street* and I was impressed by her honesty when she talked to me about her battle with anorexia.

By admitting and facing up to her problem, she almost certainly saved her own life, as well as that of other young women and young men.

Tracy's problems began when she went to drama school and someone told her she had a fat bum. That acted as a trigger for her to lose weight. She is a determined girl who was bullied at school and who always wanted to be a dancer. She went on a diet with the same determination that she gave to her dancing classes. Her dieting quickly spiralled out of control and she became anorexic. Tracy really was eating very little and also exercising frenetically to try and burn off calories. She became depressed and eventually went to see her doctor who sent her to hospital.

Tracy did start eating again, and her weight went back to a far healthier level, but she wasn't out of the woods, and she hadn't been 'cured'. Five years ago she had a relapse. Photographs at the time show a painfully thin young woman with stick-like legs and sunken cheeks. Bosses at *Coronation Street* gave her some time off and she got proper counselling, which she rightly says is the only way to a proper long-term recovery.

At her thinnest Tracy, who is five feet seven inches, weighed just five and a half stone.

She was lucky, she got help and she is now confident enough about her body to have released two salsa-cise exercise videos, and she was able to bare all in the stage play *The Blue Room*, risking comparisons with Nicole Kidman who made the role famous and was described by one drooling critic as 'theatrical Viagra'.

Tracy has come a long way, and seeing her look so well gives hope to those suffering from the illness and to their families. However, Karen Carpenter and Lena Zavaroni were not so fortunate. They were both anorexia sufferers who died because of their illness.

Karen had a voice like liquid velvet. In the seventies she and her brother Richard were enormously successful with hits like 'Top Of The World' and 'Goodbye to Love', and almost everyone I knew had a copy of their greatest hits album in their record collection.

Karen looked as if she had it all, but she died of a heart attack at the age of thirty-two, brought on because her body was wrecked by being starved of food for years. Karen wasn't a naturally slim woman – she was a healthy pear-shaped girl – but when she and her brother became famous she felt under pressure to lose weight.

Karen had very little control over her life. She felt she was dominated by those around her (something many anorexics feel) and the dieting became just about the only thing she felt she had some power over. It became obsessive and Karen would hardly eat anything. She would also take laxatives and would make herself sick. At her thinnest she weighed just five stone.

Her death in 1983 was the first time that the disease really came out of hiding. Karen wasn't the only one suffering, but because she was in the public eye it made headline news around the world, and people started talking about anorexia. There was shock and disbelief that someone with so much to live for would willingly starve herself to death.

Lena Zavaroni made her name as a child star on the show *Opportunity Knocks* in the mid-seventies. She died in 1999 at the age of thirty-five, after a battle with anorexia that lasted twenty-two years.

Lena was a cute, slightly chubby child who sang in front of the Queen and the President of the United States before she was in her teens. Her desire to lose weight began when she wasn't able to fit into the costumes being made for her. Again, like Karen, it was the classic case of the young girl with very little control over her life, apart from what she chose to eat.

I interviewed Lena not long before she died, and I will never forget how tiny and thin she was, like a sick little sparrow. She was determined to beat the illness that had blighted her life, ruined her career and her marriage, and made her deeply unhappy. She actually died in the hospital where she went to have an operation that she hoped would help her to be able to eat properly again. Her body was so weakened by years of starvation that she simply could not recover from the pneumonia that eventually killed her.

Lena and Karen are two of the most high-profile victims of the disease which can kill, but there are thousands of young people secretly starving themselves and harming their bodies. Some of them started out just wanting to be thinner, but the illness has taken them over. The consequences of virtually starving yourself are horrendous:

● You won't be able to sleep properly, and you will have constipation.

● Your concentration goes, as well as your ability to think straight.

● Depression is a very common side-effect.

● Anorexics don't just wear layers of jumpers to disguise their weight loss, they increasingly feel the cold.

● Muscles become weaker, as do bones (osteoporosis is a common side-effect of long-term anorexia).

● Your body shuts down.

● Your periods stop.

● Often a fine coating of hair covers the body.

● It can kill you.

It is highly unlikely your daughter or best friend will willingly come and tell you that she is anorexic. In fact she might think there is absolutely nothing wrong with her in the early stages. She is just 'on a diet'. However, thanks to the publicity attracted by high-profile sufferers of eating disorders, we now have an idea of what to expect:

● They will never be around at mealtimes.

● They will tell you they have already eaten.

● They are exercising much more than is normal.

● Sufferers will often wear baggy clothes to disguise their weight loss.

● They will be moody, bad tempered and irritable (more so than just the normal teenage surliness).

TREATMENT

The worst thing about seeing someone inflict this harm on themselves is the sheer sense of utter helplessness and frustration. There's no point in shouting at someone with anorexia. They will simply refuse to hear. Threats and deals don't tend to work either.

However, the quicker you get help the quicker you'll get them well.

Your GP is the first person you should contact. If you suspect someone you care about has anorexia, it will be tough to get them to admit there's a problem, in which case go to the doctor yourself and impress on him or her just how worried you are.

If the anorexia has been going on for some time, the first priority will be to get the weight back on, and to treat the kinds of illnesses that can be caused by the starvation. So it might be the case that a stay in hospital is required, which I know isn't ideal but it might be necessary.

Once the weight is back on, the hard work really begins. This will be a long hard road and there really is no miracle 'cure'. Only good counselling will get to the bottom of the problem that manifests itself as anorexia. You have to prepare yourself for a hard slog with some setbacks along the way.

One woman who has had notable success is Dee Dawson who runs Rhodes Farm in north London, a place where children aged between six and sixteen who suffer from eating disorders can live and be treated. The atmosphere is much more that of a boarding school than a hospital or institution, and children are referred from all over the country.

The whole idea is that they are treated in as normal an

environment as possible. The day is filled with lessons and activities like swimming, arts and crafts, horse riding and drama. The children are kept busy so that they have little or no time to worry about food and how much they are eating.

Rewards, like special outings, are given if they continue to gain weight. They are also given psychotherapy, and parents and family are encouraged to take part in family meetings.

Bulimia

This is a hellish illness where the sufferer goes on eating binges and then makes herself sick to get rid of the food. She may even make herself vomit after eating what only she would consider to be too much. Sufferers also use laxatives.

Bulimia is different from anorexia in that you might not be able to spot a sufferer because their weight remains constant. As the illness progresses, however, it has a devastating effect on their health.

Princess Diana was the most well-known bulimic, and by going public with her condition she broke down so many barriers and made it easier for sufferers to talk about what they were going through.

I cannot get the image out of my head of the beautiful, much envied Princess of Wales sitting on her own, eating a bowl of custard and bars of white chocolate in front of *Eastenders*. Once her favourite show was over, she would rush to the toilet, put her head down the pan and make herself vomit. Her faithful butler Paul Burrell made sure that she had plenty of soft, sweet food available, so that it could easily be thrown up later.

Bulimics have a fear of being fat and it is slightly older women in their early-to mid-twenties who tend to be affected. They operate behind closed doors, and some get so skilled at making themselves vomit that they can do it by just pressing their hand on to their stomach.

Binge eating is a classic symptom of bulimia. Sufferers will devour large quantities of food – whole loaves, whole boxes of chocolates, tubs of ice cream, an entire cake – and then throw the whole lot up again. Then they will sit on the bathroom floor sobbing their hearts out, feeling wretched, depressed and very very guilty. Bingeing and then throwing up can raise or lower a bulimic's weight by at least half a stone in a very short period of time. It plays havoc with the body and the condition eventually takes over the sufferer's life completely.

People are often shocked to learn of a friend's condition, because on the surface bulimics can seem fun to be with. They can be adventurous risk takers with a devil-may-care attitude. This is a front and hiding the fact that they are a bundle of insecurities. Underneath, bulimics are suffering from (our old pal) low self-esteem. The feelings of guilt can make them feel unworthy. They are anxious, depressed and feel disgusted with themselves.

WHAT BULIMIA DOES TO YOUR BODY

● The enamel on your teeth will dissolve because of the stomach acid you are vomiting up.

● Your face will puff up because your salivary glands swell.

- Your heartbeat can become irregular.
- Your muscles get weaker.
- You can damage your kidneys.
- You could suffer from epileptic fits.
- Using too many laxatives gives you persistent stomach pain, swells your fingers up, and wrecks your bowel muscles so that you will suffer from long-term constipation.

Bulimia isn't as easy to spot as anorexia and it can take longer for people close to the sufferer to realise something is horribly wrong. Often there's no real decrease in weight to ring alarm bells.

SIGNS FOR FRIENDS AND FAMILY TO LOOK OUT FOR

As this illness tends to affect slightly older women they tend to be living on their own, so they can binge and vomit in secret. In fact bulimia would be hard to disguise in a normal family environment, although some young girls do manage it. Look out for food that goes missing, empty wrappers in the bedroom, smells and signs of vomiting.

Again your GP is the first port of call. As with anorexia, people with bulimia need professional help and a lot of patience and understanding.

TREATMENT

I find it utterly heartbreaking that thousands of bright young women and men are living lives of utter desperation, trapped by their eating disorder. They should be having the time of their lives; instead they risk long-term health problems and even death. It is a shocking waste of all their talent, and the media and the fashion industry have to shoulder some of the blame.

Eva Herzigova is an example of what the twisted world of fashion can do to even the most beautiful young person. The woman whose bosoms once made men want to burst into song, and who starred in the famous Wonderbra billboard campaign that almost caused traffic chaos, was photographed at the beginning of 2003 looking like something from a concentration camp.

The curves were gone, she was stick thin, scrawny and ill looking. Her formerly peachy, glowing skin was patched with blotches of red and white. She had spots and cold sores, and looked dead behind the eyes.

While the rest of the world was shocked at the change in such a stunning young woman, Eva was actually signed up for a fashion shoot with a posh magazine, thus sending out the message loud and clear that the only way for models to have a career is to starve themselves.

While the fashion industry actively promotes this kind of 'heroin chic', our young women will continue to stop eating, thinking that they will then become beautiful and desirable.

- If you suspect your child or your friend has an eating disorder, then get help as soon as you can.
- If caught quickly, the sufferer has a much better chance of getting better.
- They will need a lot of help, support, patience and understanding because there is no quick fix solution.

COSMETIC SURGERY

None of us are lucky enough to have a painting in the attic that gets older while we remain firm and beautiful, but then Dorian Grey never had the chance to have liposuction.

Having plastic surgery is becoming as common in the States as changing your hair colour. We in the UK are slightly more reserved – but that hasn't stopped the cosmetic-surgery business booming. We are now spending over two hundred million pounds a year on having our boobs enlarged, our butts lifted and our noses bobbed.

Of course, there are those who have surgery to rectify the effects of an accident or illness. However, the vast majority do it for reasons of vanity and in order to look younger. I do think that cosmetic surgery has a role to play if someone is deeply unhappy with how they look and if it will give them a confidence boost and make them feel better about themselves, but I draw the line at procedures where naïve and vulnerable individuals expect that a nose job will turn their life around and make everything wonderful.

For years, women in Thailand and Hong Kong have been demanding surgery on their eyes to make them more round and 'Western'. There has also been a huge increase in breast implants in Asia. This is purely due to pressure from movies and magazines and I think it is very sad. In the States there is a worrying trend for people to walk into a surgeon's office clutching a photograph of their favourite star and demanding to be made to look just like them.

Despite advances in technology, this is not yet possible and if your surgeon is reputable he will tell you so, and will also spend a lot of time with you explaining the operation, the risks and the outcome you can expect. Beware, however. There are unscrupulous surgeons who will perform serial operations on people who really need proper help and counselling, and who have deep-rooted problems that will not be cured by going under the knife.

Michael Jackson is, of course, the prime example. He suffered terribly from acne when he was younger. It's a crippling enough condition for anyone going through puberty, but how much worse for someone in the public eye know as 'cute little Michael'. Sadly, Jackson's father mocked his son's spotty face and also used to call him 'big nose', declaiming that he didn't get any of it from *his* side of the family.

Michael was desperately starved of parental affection, and we can all see the effects of the scorn heaped on him by his father. It's as plain as the nose that used to be on his face.

Jackson hated his looks so much that he has completely transformed himself, and the result is horrible. Personally, I think the surgeons responsible should never be allowed to work on anyone again. He still maintains he has only had surgical procedures to his nose to make him breathe more easily. If he really does believe that then for me he is an even sadder figure than I thought.

Melanie Griffith is another example of someone who I think has completely ruined her looks by far too much surgery. Melanie is married to Antonio Banderas, one of the world's most desirable men I think you would agree. He fell in love with a beautiful, confident vibrant woman, but she has made herself look ridiculous, particularly by using collagen to pump up her lips. The catfish look is not attractive and a concerned Antonio has forbidden her to have any more surgery.

Closer to home, Leslie Ash made herself look utterly ridiculous with a procedure to pump up her lips that resulted in the infamous 'trout pout' that turned a very pretty woman into an object of pity and ridicule. It reminded me of the time Lynn Perrie, who played (poison) Ivy Tilsley in *Coronation Street*, turned up on the set with lips like two jumbo-sized hot dogs, that appeared to me to have a life all of their own. I think she looked plain daft, and soon packed her bags and left the street. However, neither Lynn nor Leslie have put women off having painful lip surgery. It is one of the most common and popular ways of trying to look younger. It is also one of the most obvious of all the cosmetic procedures, and when it does go wrong you look like you've been hit in the face with a very heavy shovel.

Obviously, we would all like to look young and beautiful for ever and ever – not all women are as lucky as Lauren Bacall, Sophia Loren and Joan Collins, who have aged gracefully and who look better now than they did in their youth. Because we live in a society that worships youth, all that lifting, tucking and pumping is about trying to turn the clock back, but too many women end up with that look of total and utter surprise (also known as the wind-tunnel effect) which is far uglier than a few laughter lines and baggy eyes.

When I was a youngster, someone aged fifty plus was considered well over the hill – it was when women had a grey perm and a shapeless frock, and let their facial hair grow where it may. Now, of course, a woman is in her prime in her late thirties, forties and fifties – at the peak of her sexual allure and with the confidence and self-belief she didn't possess in the teenage pre-cellulite years. I don't think there's necessarily anything wrong with a little nip and tuck to make you look 'refreshed', although I am too much of a coward to consider cosmetic surgery myself. As long as you go to a proper surgeon and your expectations are reasonable ones, then you will almost certainly be happy with the result.

However, too many people clutching their photograph of Jennifer Lopez are devastated when they have paid out a fortune and endured weeks or even months of suffering to discover that they don't look as good as they thought they would.

I just do not think cosmetic surgery should be used as a way of running away from more deep-seated problems.

This is the big one and you really have to have total trust in your surgeon, and to know exactly what you are letting yourself in for.

If you have thought about this long and hard, and are convinced that you and your surgeon know what it is you want, and he has given you a *realistic* idea of what you will look like afterwards, then you have done all you can to protect yourself.

Usually, women tend to think about facelifts in their forties, fifties and sixties. Surgeons agree that generally a woman who has a facelift at the age of forty-five will have a better result than a woman of fifty-five, because her skin will be more elastic and of a better quality. She'll also recover more quickly. However, everyone is different and we all have different pain thresholds.

Having seen a facelift operation on TV, I would rather eat dirt than have my face peeled off and tugged up, but I have been lucky enough to inherit my mother's and my grandmother's good skin and I'm still in pretty good shape for a woman in her forties. I know that for other women a facelift is what they want and they are determined to go ahead. What you want to achieve from your operation is not people saying, 'Oh my God, you've had a facelift,' but 'Oh my God, you look so well and so rested and so much younger.'

Expect a long recovery process – up to half a year in some cases.

BOTOX

I do find it extraordinary that women will pay for someone to inject their face with a poisonous substance that means they can no longer register emotion.

We scoff at Elizabethan women who used to paint their faces white and ended up with lead poisoning, but, bizarrely, botox parties have sprung up across the land, where women have a few glasses of champers while a doctor injects their laughter lines with a toxic substance, and we don't really know what the long-term effects could be!

In fact, in February 2003, a leading doctor in the US warned that botox could lead to more wrinkles than it erased. What apparently happens is that the facial muscles which are still working (and haven't been frozen) overcompensate, and you end up with wrinkles where you really shouldn't have them.

So think before you get that jab full of toxic gunk.

This trend might be on the way out though, at least among actors and actresses. Big name directors have been refusing to work with thespians who have been botoxed because they are unable to express the range of emotions required to make their performances realistic.

Obviously, all daytime soap actors in the US are exempt.

LIPOSUCTION

Having the fat Hoovered out of your bum, tum and thighs sounds like the answer to all your prayers. However, you must be cautious with this procedure. It should never be used as a way to lose weight, and should only ever be carried out by a real professional on places where stubborn fat just refuses to budge. The most common areas that are surgically vacuumed are the outer thighs and stomach for women. Men tend to get their 'love handles' done.

As with all procedures, you have to be realistic and not have too high expectations.

There are risks, this is a surgical procedure and you will have to be treated under general anaesthetic, with all the attendant dangers. You can also get infections, bleeding and nerve damage. The skin may not look smooth and you could end up with a kind of waviness if too much fat is removed (a bit like the sea shore when the tide has gone out). It's also painful and it's not cheap – but if you are utterly determined to go ahead, make sure you visit a surgeon who knows what he is doing.

In 2002, Denise Hendry, the wife of former Scottish foot-ball captain Colin Hendry, went in for what she thought was a fairly routine liposuction procedure to get rid of a little roll of fat on her tummy. The operation went horribly wrong. Denise developed septicaemia and went into a coma. Colin thought she would die, and for a while her life was in the balance. She is on the road to recovery now, but she is lucky to be alive.

On my TV show, we followed one woman's progress in having liposuction on her thighs. She had lost a lot of weight after having children, but, despite exercise and eating prop-erly, the fat on her thighs just would not budge.

She went to a very respectable surgeon, paid three thou-sand pounds for the operation, and came back to see us one week later. She had to wear very unsexy elasticised tight long knickers that covered her thighs and she was in a lot of pain, but six weeks later she had the thighs she had always wanted.

The fat won't go back on to her thighs – but if she goes back to overeating and being a couch potato, it will go on other areas of the body.

Liposuction is *not* the lazy way to lose weight. You can't tell yourself that you will have your belly and your bum vacuumed for your fortieth or fiftieth birthday, and meanwhile pass the chocolate cake. It doesn't work like that. It is major invasive surgery and you must weigh up the risks.

BREAST ENLARGEMENT

Unless you have virtually no bosom, or you have been left with two empty paper bags in place of your perky boobs due to child bearing, I really don't think you should consider this operation. You can always tell when a woman has had implants and Hollywood heartthrob Colin Farrell described the feeling of caressing them as being like stroking a rock.

However, if you really feel self-conscious about having little or no boobies then make sure you choose a reputable surgeon who has done this op before, and who can show you plenty of before and after pictures.

It's also a good idea to try and talk to other people who have had the operation, and to find out exactly how painful it is and how long it takes to recover. Also ask them if you can have a right good look at the finished result. (This clearly depends on how well you know them.)

I do believe this operation is fantastic if you have had breast cancer and have decided to have reconstruction. It can certainly help in the recovery process of some women who have had to have a mastectomy. Of course not all women opt to have reconstruction.

There is one South American woman who has good cause to be delighted with her rock-hard silicon breasts.

Jane Selma Soares from Rio de Janeiro in Brazil was caught up in a shooting between police officers and drug traffickers in the city in January 2003. She tried to hide, but a bullet caught her in the chest. She was taken to hospital but found to have no serious injury – her silicon implants had stopped the bullet from entering further into her body and damaging her internal organs.

BREAST REDUCTION

I have a friend who had *enormous* bosoms which suddenly appeared overnight, like a couple of Exocet missiles, when she was just fourteen. They made her life a bit of a misery, especially when she was younger. Boys would never look her in the eye, and she felt as if her breasts were the only things they were interested in. (As we are talking teenage boys here she was probably right.) She suffered horrible back pain from carrying around these massive mammaries, and she could never get clothes to fit. She was also heartily sick of all the Dolly Parton-style jokes. In fact, like Dolly, she used to tell them first – no you really don't get many of these to the pound, and yes, I do have tiny feet because nothing grows in the shade, etc etc.

When she was twenty-five, she had her boobs reduced from a 36 EE to a 36 C. It was a painful procedure, and cost her around three thousand pounds, but it did change her life for the better. She had the operation done instead of buying a car, and she's more than happy with that deal.

NOSE JOB

This really can make a huge difference to your self-confidence, and if you have the right surgeon who gives you the right result then it can be life-changing.

Natasha Richardson had a nose job when she left drama school and it turned her life around. Because she was more confident, she won bigger and better roles and also managed to attract the divine Liam Neeson. The two of them have one of the happiest marriages in La La land and two lovely kids.

Of course it wasn't her new nose that dictated her acting abilities and her attractiveness, but it was all to do with what the operation meant to her and the difference it made to her self-esteem. This is what can happen with what I would call 'responsible' cosmetic surgery, where you think long and hard about the operation, and you have a lengthy consultation with your surgeon. Some of them even have computer graphics so you can see what you will look like with your new nose – but be wary of the person who says he can make you ravishingly beautiful. Your expectations should be reasonable and achievable.

The trouble with cosmetic surgery is that you can usually tell it has been done, unless you get a very, very good surgeon and are willing to pay through your brand new nose.

Bottom lifts have become every popular, especially in the USA, and it is all down to Jennifer
Lopez and her glorious backside.

BUMS

This operation is a bit like breast enlargement, as silicon
implants are inserted into the buttocks. It is a new procedure
that only the very vain and very rich should be subjecting
themselves to, and it means you won't be able to sit down
comfortably for a very long time.

Stick a couple of bean bags down your butt, or invest in
those bum-lifting knickers and tights instead. They're a
whole lot cheaper and a lot less pain.

A disturbing and rather gruesome new line in
plastic surgery is the increase in operations on
willies and fannies – or penile augmentation

YOUR NAUGHTY BITS

and designer vaginas to give them their 'proper' names. Why
would any man want to put himself and his willy through
such pain and torture, unless, of course, he has been unfor-
tunate enough to have been bobbited? (Remember the wife
who cut off her hubbie's penis in a fit of rage about his infidelity, and then drove off and flung the severed member out
of the car window?)

However, it seems there are a lot of men out there who
will try anything to get a bigger one.

Basically, the enlargement is effected by removing fat
from one part of the body and injecting it into the shaft of
the penis. (As only a fathead would want to have this done,
maybe it is taken from the area around his thick skull.)

If all goes well, he will be the proud owner of a bigger

dick. However, complications range from infection and bleeding to 'contour irregularities' – that is, it looks weird. Also, there's no evidence that this procedure will be permanent, and the injected fat could be reabsorbed into the body after just a few months, which means all that pain, suffering and expense was all for nothing. Unless you have an itsy-bitsy-teeny-weeny willy this operation is not even to be contemplated.

Vaginal surgery is much more disturbing.

If you feel that your front bottom is somehow 'disfigured', and it really truly worries you, then maybe, just maybe, you would have a case for being operated on – but let's be honest, if your vagina was that 'unusual', and was affecting your self-confidence to such a degree, you'd probably be able to get the operation on the NHS.

However, there are now operations available, especially in the USA, which claim to give that 'Barbie doll' look to the female genitals – neat, tidy and virtually invisible. This is conforming to an ideal of the adult female body that doesn't exist. We all know that if Barbie was real she would not be able to stand up. The weight of her breasts would make her fall over, and the size of her torso means there is nowhere for her to keep her internal organs. Likewise her vagina – it just isn't there. Is that what we really want grown women to look like?

As with the ops on the penis, I believe these procedures are taking advantage of unhappy, insecure people who don't need surgery; they just need a bit more confidence, self-esteem and a considerate, understanding lover.

Spare the knife

There are now countless anti-ageing treatments on the market, including non-surgical procedures that you can have in beauty salons. They cost a lot of money and some are better than others, but if they give you a bit of a boost and you can afford to treat yourself now and again – then why not? At a less expensive level, Cindy Crawford vigorously rubs ground coffee into her thighs as a treatment and preventative for cellulite, and Shania Twain swears by a certain moisturising cream that you won't find in any swanky store in Manhattan – she uses the same kind that farmers put on the udders of their cows to stop them getting all cracked and sore. Judging by Shania's glowing complexion, the stuff works beautifully.

To be honest, the best anti-ageing beauty tip I was ever given was from Joan Collins, who believes that we should *never* sunbathe. La Collins always protects herself. Invest in a moisturiser with sunscreen, and get that floppy hat on your head, or by the time you are fifty you'll be like a crocodile skin handbag.

Lorraine's Lifelines

- If you are determined to have cosmetic work done, make sure you are doing it for the right reasons.
- Make sure you go to a reputable surgeon.
- Do not be afraid to ask for references, and to look at before and after pictures.
- Be realistic. Remember that Michael Jackson wanted to look like Diana Ross and instead he resembles Peter Pan's rather strange auntie.

DEALING WITH STRESS

Stress is one of the great buzzwords of modern life and is used as a catch-all to describe a whole range of problems.

Basically, stress is what happens when you are up against it and aren't convinced you can meet the challenge. It is also what happens when you get yourself into the habit of doing things that make you unhappy.

This sounds very simple, but it means, for example, that you could be overworked to the point of wanting to run away because you cannot cope any more, or conversely you could be so bored out of your tiny mind that you just want to scream.

The most stressful job I ever had was working as a researcher at the BBC. There were four of us in the one room, sharing a single telephone, and we were supposed to investigate and set up stories that would be covered in the teatime news programme. We had all left good jobs (I was a journalist on the *East Kilbride News*) and were on short-term six-month contracts. No one really knew what to do with us, and we had to make ourselves indispensable to prove that we were needed. For the first few months we floundered around and didn't really have enough to do. I found this almost unbearable, and quickly found myself feeling blue, not sleeping at night and getting edgy. Eventually things settled down, but I remember the panicky feelings vividly and work was a nightmare.

> *During my four years as a reporter, I was on constant call and covered the likes of the Piper Alpha disaster and Lockerbie.*

I coped far better when I changed jobs and became the reporter covering Scotland for TVam, even though it meant I was on call twenty-four hours a day, seven days a week.

A typical day might involve getting up at the crack of dawn to let a guest into the Glasgow studio for a live link to the London studio. They'd need a cup of tea and a pep talk, and afterwards be sent off in a taxi home. Then, having compiled a list of important events happening in Scotland and a list of ideas for up-and-coming features, I'd talk to the regional editor and set off to cover the story of the day. I'd sort out the interviews, locations and travel. We might have to drive for fourteen hours for one fifteen-second sound bite.

During my four years as a reporter, I was on constant call and covered the likes of the Piper Alpha disaster and Lockerbie.

I met my future husband when he joined the crew in Glasgow, and after a year of circling round each other we eventually started living together. Everyone was amazed at how fast we would be on the scene of any news story, especially in the middle of the night, but of course our bleepers would go off at the same time (always a good thing in any relationship) and we'd jump in the car and be off.

Often we were up all day and all night, especially in the middle of a big story, but I seemed to manage on very little sleep, and adrenaline gets you through. I was also a lot younger and we didn't have any children, so I could be totally focused on the job. I found the hectic pace far easier to deal with than my time at the BBC, and was much happier and less stressed.

> *Being stuck in a routine you find stifling and unchallenging can be as stressful as having too much to do.*

Stress has become associated with a harassed businessman in the city who is trying to pull down deals, keep his mistress satisfied and pay his wife's clothes bill, but I would define real stress as dealing with three kids under five if you have an absent or unemployed husband and a part-time job paying the minimum wage.

It can be just as stressful being at home, perhaps with a new baby, if you've been used to being out at work. Being stuck in a routine you find stifling and unchallenging can be as stressful as having too much to do.

Things that make you stressed

OTHER PEOPLE If you are going through a bad patch in your marriage, or you are fighting with the kids or your mother-in-law, or maybe the neighbours are driving you nuts with their loud music – all of that can make you stressed and it builds up like a volcano that has to blow.

WORK As I have said, you are just as likely to suffer from stress if you are in a dull unfulfilling job as you would in a hectic, demanding draining occupation. Your boss and your fellow workers can cause stress (see the section on being bullied in the workplace on page 142).

Perhaps you find yourself overwhelmed with work, but ask yourself this: Are you overworked or just badly organised? I know loads of people who sit at untidy desks piled high with papers and who are always harassed and late for every single meeting. They aren't actually doing an effective job. They are simply disorganised. Often these are the people who are first into the office in the morning and the last to leave at night, but they aren't achieving all that much, apart from giving themselves an ulcer.

The good news for them is that being disorganised is a relatively easy problem to fix – should they be willing to try. I don't think an untidy desk is a sign of being 'creative' and neither should anyone else. Get it tidied and sorted.

To stop things getting back to a complete mess, you have

to learn to prioritise. Do the tough stuff first. It gets it out of the way and there's no point in putting it off and having it hanging over you.

I receive loads of letters through my work in TV and for newspapers, and I am very glad that I do. It is a brilliant way to see what people think and what subjects matter to them. However, correspondence can pile up and become overwhelming, so I always try to keep on top of it. My granny always taught me it was polite to reply to people who have been kind enough to write to you, so I feel it would be letting her down as well as all the viewers and readers not to get back to them as quickly as I can. There's always the difficult-to-answer letter that I'm tempted to put to the bottom of the pile, but I know that I have to answer them all eventually and there's no point in delaying my reply. Spending an hour a day on correspondance makes sure I don't get snowed under.

If you are really overwhelmed with work, learn to delegate whenever you possibly can. Give people a chance to help you and don't stand over their shoulder while they do the work. It's also important to make sure you switch off when you get home. Work should not be the centre of your life, or what will you do if you lose your job or when you retire? Make sure you have a 'hinterland' – whether it is gardening, painting or collecting teaspoons.

SLEEP

Are you getting enough sleep?

Take it from someone who knows that lack of proper sleep is meat and drink to the stress monster. You should be trying to get seven to eight hours a night, and it needs to be uninterrupted.

As someone who jealously hoards every hour of sleep I can get, I have come up with a few tried and tested methods to get a decent night's rest.

First of all make sure that your bed is up to scratch. If it is too old, soft, small or hard, you really should be thinking about a replacement. Are those pillows also a bit on the ancient side? New research has revealed that 10 per cent of the weight of a pillow can be made up of dead skin cells and hair from our heads. So maybe invest in a crisp clean new pillow or two.

Don't eat too much before going to bed, and don't be tempted to have a nightcap – booze keeps you awake.

Make sure your bedroom is a relaxing haven – don't have work stuff in there – and it's not a good idea to watch TV before trying to go to sleep. Reading isn't a great idea either. If you start a new Maeve Binchy you'll be up until the wee small hours because you just *have* to know the ending.

Regular, gentle exercise during the day helps you sleep, but don't do anything vigorous just before bed. (That includes sex I'm afraid, but then again, some people swear that it sends them off to sleep, and as long as it isn't during the act, I suppose that's OK.)

Don't lie in bed awake and festering – if you really can't get to sleep and you are tossing and turning, get up and do something to unwind. A long warm bath with lots of gorgeous aromatherapy bubbles is lovely, or you could listen to a relaxation tape.

If you have tried everything and are truly at the end of your tether, go and see your GP. He or she may prescribe sleeping pills, but remember these should only be for the short term.

Are you eating properly?

FOOD

If you exist on a diet of fast food, coffee and general rubbish, your body won't have the proper fuel to help you deal with everyday life. You need to arm yourself with a good healthy diet that includes lots of fresh fruit and vegetables if you want to go into battle with stress.

MONEY WORRIES

Anxiety about not being able to pay the bills can keep you awake at night, especially if you don't feel you have anyone to share your worries with.

If you really can't talk to your partner or a pal about your finances because you feel ashamed to admit there's a problem, then get down to the bank, building society or Citizens Advice Bureau. Don't try and ignore the problem or it will just get worse.

It's a really good idea to write down your expenditure. Divide a sheet of paper in half and on one side list all your outgoings: the rent or mortgage, fuel, bills, food, travel costs and treats. On the other list your income. Now see if there is anywhere you can make some cuts. Is it possible to walk sometimes instead of taking the bus or the car? Could you give up the fags, bars of chocolate or new clothes – just until you get back on your feet? It might be time for a bit of plastic surgery, and you may have to get a pair of scissors and cut those credit cards and store cards in half.

Like every other problem in the world, the longer you leave it, the tougher it is to sort out, but whatever you do, please think long and hard and explore all other avenues before borrowing money from those ads on the TV. You will end up paying vast sums of interest for what appears to be a small loan.

Stress is a cunning beast and can disguise itself as other ailments.

If you are tired, feeling blue, short-tempered, having bad dreams and just generally feeling that life is rotten, then more than likely you are suffering from stress.

If you just can't be bothered making love, then it might not be that you no longer fancy your partner. Loss of libido is a classic symptom of stress.

You might also suffer from headaches, constipation and mouth ulcers. Being run down is a very common indicator that you are overloaded, and the danger is that you get to the stage of the car with no petrol and you are running on empty.

Something has to give. You have to make sure you spot the signs before it gets that bad.

It's OK to have a blub now and again. If things really are getting on top of you there is absolutely nothing wrong with having a good old-fashioned weep. It might not change anything, and you'll be left with red eyes and a shiny nose, but I guarantee you will feel better. However if you constantly feel teary, on edge and irritable, then you have a problem and you need help.

Try and be more flexible. So many people suffer from the stress of dealing with things that come up in their lives that they just cannot adapt to. Life is all about changes and some you just cannot foresee – like a death in the family, a job change or an unplanned pregnancy. These are *huge* events and won't be easy to deal with. So do not be afraid to ask for help!

Try not to get too het up about things you have no control over. Remember that something is only stressful if you allow it to be, and your attitude to the situation will be the deciding factor.

There's nothing wrong with being nervous in certain situations, but you mustn't let the fear overwhelm you. For example, say you are going for an interview for a new job that you really want. It is fine to be nervous, but if you convince yourself it is all going to go horribly wrong and worry yourself sick, then you will be completely stressed out and you will make your worst fears become a reality and you won't get the job. If, however, you think positively and make sure you have prepared yourself properly for the interview and that you look your best, you will have a far better chance of succeeding.

Overcoming stress

If you are feeling stressed you have to ask yourself a very basic question – will what you are fretting about matter in a year's time? Very few things other than a serious illness affecting yourself, your friends or family will actually have any real importance at the end of twelve months.

Also, do not put off until tomorrow what you can do today. As I have said, putting tough stuff aside just doesn't work. Deal with things as they happen and don't let things pile up – whether it is difficult clients or problems at work or the full ironing basket at home.

Breathe! I know we all have to do it or we'd die – but taking deep breaths really does help in the fight against stress. Breathe in, count to three (slowly) and breathe out. Do this ten times and you will feel calmer and more in control. You can do it anywhere (like those strange women who tell you to do your pelvic floor exercises when you are waiting in the bus queue). You can do your deep breaths in the loo, while waiting for the kettle to boil, in the lift – anywhere.

I was on a flight to New York recently and they had this amazing relaxation tape. A man with the most incredibly seductive and relaxing voice was telling me to breathe and relax and picture myself on a beach. He told me to start at the top of my head and work my way down, relaxing my neck, arms, chest, stomach and legs, right down to my toes. It was the most relaxing half hour I have ever spent. I have always been a bit sceptical about relaxation tapes, but this really worked.

Take some time out and *do not* feel guilty about it. You have to be able to recharge your batteries or you will just be like a coil that gets wound up so tight that one day it snaps.

Stress can turn into depression if you don't nip it in the bud, so here are some more ways to combat it.

Stressbusters

Find time for yourself, even if it is only ten minutes a day when you are doing your exercises. (You have decided to do them haven't you?)

One of my very favourite stressbusters is putting on a good loud piece of music and pretending to be the lead singer in the band – it could be anyone from Robert Smith in the Cure to Kylie. You need to have the house to yourself so that you don't get interrupted by a laughing husband or giggling daughter. It is amazing how much better you feel once you've pretended to be live at Wembley.

I know I am probably far too much like Monica from *Friends*, but I do find that I feel better if the cupboards are in order – and doing a really big clear-out is very therapeutic. I feel more in control when everything's organised. Of course things soon get messed up again, but I enjoy opening orderly cupboards and drawers for a couple of days.

I've already told you about walking as a way to keep fit, but it is a brilliant way to unwind as well, as are the long hot baths I mentioned, especially with some aromatherapy oils, bubble bath, a few candles and a good book.

Aromatherapy massage – if you can afford it – is one of the most wonderful stressbusters. If anyone wants to give you the perfect birthday or Christmas gift ask them for a session with your local aromatherapist.

Good company can dispel stress. Get together with members of your family or your pals who make you laugh. If you have to be on your own, then hire a Billy Connolly video, put the phone off the hook, and let yourself roar with laughter.

It's a very good idea to make a list of things that cause you stress, because then you can work out ways to avoid such situations in the first place.

Finally – I can't say it often enough – don't be afraid to ask for help.

Lorraine's Lifelines

- Make time for yourself – even if it is only five minutes.
- Going for a walk costs nothing, burns off fat and is a terrific stressbuster.
- Get organised.
- Try a relaxation tape.
- Spend time with people who make you laugh.
- Ask for help – don't be a martyr.

4
RELATIONSHIPS

How we get on with each other – whether it is our husband, lover, best friend, relatives, neighbours or people in the work-place – can obviously have a huge impact on our lives and determine our happiness.

You get out of relationships what you put in, so again it is down to *you* to make the most of all your dealings with the people around you.

FINDING YOUR SOUL MATE

This is what we all strive for – that one person who, as Tom Cruise said to Renee Zellweger in the movie *Jerry Maguire*, is the other human being in this big wide world that 'completes you'.

We spend an awful lot of time, effort and energy looking for this person. Talking to my thirty-something single friends, it is clear that it is pretty tough out there. Unless you have met the man you are going to settle down with at school, college or university, or at work, then it just gets harder and harder as the years go by. The older you get, the more the 'baggage' that comes with the person who you end up dating – in the form of ex-wives, children, girl-friends and bad experiences in love. On the other hand, however, perhaps they are also wiser, more patient, appreciative and respon-sible – so it's by no means all doom and gloom.

Women's expectations are much higher than they used to be – and while that is no bad thing, there's a tendency for many women to have a very rigid idea in their minds of their 'Mr Right'. He has to look a certain way, dress a certain way, hold down a well-paid job and be a perfect gentleman while also being a New Man who is in touch with his feminine side. Outside the movies, this kind of paragon really doesn't exist.

One of my friends thought she had met the 'perfect' man who had just moved into her block of flats. He was handsome, funny and good company. They went for a drink and really seemed to hit it off. Two weeks later it was all off because she discovered he was 'too neat'. His flat was like a showroom and she felt she couldn't kick off her shoes and relax. There was a place for everything and everything in its place. The CDs were in alphabetical order and his clothes were colour co-ordinated. While some women would find that a refreshing change from dirty underpants on the bathroom floor and toothpaste all over the sink, she felt horribly uncomfortable. Maybe five years ago she could have put up with his foibles, but they are both so set in their ways that neither of them would compromise. She thought he was a fusspot and he thought she was a slattern. She broke it off and now has to play hide and seek to avoid meeting him in the lift or at the bin shelter.

Sometimes your Mr Right can be under your nose

I was friends with my husband for about a year and we got to know each other really well before we started going out together.

I met him through work when I was a reporter for TVam and he was one of the crew. I think almost from the very first we both 'fancied' each other but didn't do anything about it, until one night we went on a shoot to Glencoe to film the work of the mountain-rescue team up there.

We stayed in the Kings House Hotel, one of the oldest hotels in Scotland, right in the middle of the Glen, surrounded by some of the most splendid scenery you are ever likely to see – all very romantic.

That night we were taught the joys of 'Alabama slammers' by some of the rescue workers (those who weren't on call I hasten to add). This involves a small shot glass, a big measure of tequila, and ginger ale. You put your hand over the glass, slam it down on the bar and knock back the fizzing booze in a oner. A couple of slammers and it is instant oblivion. We both ended up in the same bedroom, but were too sozzled to do anything about it.

The next day, Steve invited me to go and see Dundee United play Hearts at Tannadice (United's home ground). It was an unusual chat-up line, I am sure you will agree, and one that I couldn't possibly decline. We have been together ever since.

Like most couples we do have our ups and downs – but essentially we like and respect each other and he makes me laugh. I found the person I wanted to spend the rest of my life with, and I do feel incredibly lucky.

Romances in the workplace don't always have happy endings. Going out with colleagues can be very awkward if you work in a small place and then you split up. If you do start dating someone you will have to see every Monday to Friday, and who might be sharing office space, the canteen and the lift with you, do make sure that the relationship has a half decent chance of lasting longer than the fag break.

Being set-up

Well-meaning friends, especially those who are in relationships, might try and match-make for you. While this can
sometimes work, the success rate really isn't all that impressive and there's nothing worse than feeling you have been
set-up.

One of my friends is always being invited to things where
she is the only single girl and there is only one 'spare' man.
If he is a decent bloke they can have a bit of a laugh about
being thrown together by 'smug marrieds' – but she has
spent countless evenings racking her brains for topics of conversation with surly or tongue-tied men who clearly have no
interest in her and who can't wait to make their excuses and
leave. It's not that she isn't attractive, but they are probably
as cross as she is about being set-up.

But it can work.

My friend Janice managed to 'engineer' her brother to go
out with one of her friends from work. She invited them
round to her house for a few drinks before Christmas, along
with about a dozen other friends from work and some of the
neighbours. Janice really hoped they would get on. Her
brother is rather shy and hasn't had much success with
women since a long-term relationship collapsed a couple of
years ago. Her work mate had only recently joined the company and didn't know many people. Janice really liked her
and thought she seemed a bit lonely.

It wasn't an obvious set-up, but Janice worked very hard
indeed to get the two of them together and to keep them

talking. Her friend eventually asked him out for a drink (brave girl) and they have been going out with each other ever since. Things are going well and they even managed to have a laugh about the 'set-up' when Janice told them.

If you want to help your single mates, throw a party with a couple of others who are unattached and don't make it too glaringly obvious.

Breaking the Ice

It's not easy going up to a total stranger in a club or pub and trying to strike up a conversation with them. Most men revert to chat-up lines and there are some truly terrible ones out there. My least favourite is 'How do you like your eggs in the morning – fertilised or unfertilised?' If someone had ever said that to me, I would have had to nip them very hard indeed.

Other howlers that have been tried (unsuccessfully) on friends of mine include:

'If I could rearrange the alphabet I'd put U and I together', and 'Would you touch me so I can tell all my friends I have been touched by an angel?'

Chat-up lines are usually pretty gruesome, but you have to start somewhere, especially if you are in a bar or a club. The old faithful of 'Can I buy you a drink?' might not set the heather on fire for originality, but you will soon know if the person is interested or not.

If someone has plucked up the courage to talk to you and

you aren't remotely interested, turn them down firmly but politely. No one likes to be made a fool of, but you shouldn't give them hope where none exists. When you've established contact, the most important thing is to be yourself, be as natural as possible, and be interested in what the other person is saying. Always be polite, and it helps if you don't take yourself too seriously.

Finally, don't forget that this is the twenty-first century, so women don't have to wait to be 'chatted up' anymore. We can take the initiative if we want to.

Protect yourself

If you do happen to meet someone at work, through friends or even in the bus queue, and you like them and they suggest going for a drink or a meal, for goodness' sake be careful.

I am not for a minute suggesting that you should view all men as potential bastards, but you do have to be on your guard and be sensible.

In the pub or restaurant never, ever leave your drink unattended – it could be tampered with. (This also goes for those nights out with the girls when you might be letting your hair down and drinking more than you would normally.)

Lots of young women are now drinking bottles of already mixed drinks like Moscow Mules or Bacardi Breezers, because they are much more difficult to spike, and you can hold them with your thumb over the top.

When I did my radio show I spoke to a woman who very bravely told me how she had gone to a meeting in the bar of a hotel with men she thought were potential clients for the company where she worked.

The men were bogus and the whole thing was a set-up. During the meeting they spiked her drink. The next thing she knew was that it was the following morning and she was lying naked in a strange hotel room, feeling as if she had the worst hangover in the world. Her whole body, inside and out, ached and she felt sick, light headed and had no memory of what had happened the night before. She knew that she'd been raped and sexually assaulted, but she couldn't remember anything.

Somehow she got home, ran a bath and sobbed her heart out.

When she did eventually blurt out to a friend what had happened to her, the drug in her system had disappeared and was untraceable, so there was no evidence she had been drugged. No one remembered the men she was with and there was very little the police could do.

Her life has been all but destroyed. It is going to take a long time for her to get over something so traumatic, especially as she feels so helpless because the men were never caught and are more than likely doing this to other innocent, unsuspecting women.

Utter swines who spike women's drinks with drugs like Rophynol are relatively few and far between. The trouble is that we don't have clear figures because so many women don't report what has happened to them to the police.

I don't want to scare you, but the danger is out there and you do need to be careful.

Equally, if you answer a lonely hearts' advert in the newspaper, or on the Internet, it is sensible to take precautions.

Don't tell him to meet you at home, and don't give him your address or phone number. Meet somewhere neutral like a pub or restaurant where people know you.

You could get a friend to give you a call half an hour into the date, which gives you the chance to reply with a 'secret code' to alert them that you need to make your escape if he is truly appalling, or boring you to tears, or you feel uncomfortable.

Even if you are getting on well, just be on your guard. It's better to hurt his feelings by refusing a lift on the first date and making your own way home, than opening yourself up to danger.

Again, I don't want you to feel paranoid, but you just have to be responsible. For instance, don't drink too much, even if you are nervous. A slobbering drunken woman is not only horribly unattractive, but being totally pissed obviously makes you more vulnerable.

By the way I wouldn't ever recommend sleeping with someone on the first date, for all kinds of reasons.

First of all, you don't know each other well enough, and when you sleep with someone you are effectively sleeping with all the other lovers they have had when it comes to diseases like HIV, gonorrhoea and chlamydia. These diseases are all on the increase, especially among young straight men and women. Not very romantic I know, but you have to think about that before you start exchanging bodily fluids.

Call me old-fashioned, but I believe you need to know someone well before sex actually means anything. If you are able to have sex with a virtual stranger for the sheer pleasure of it and to walk away the next day with not a single regret, then that's fine for you – but I don't think many people, especially women, are really like that.

If you are planning on having sex, for God's sake use contraception. Condoms are best, not just to stop you becoming pregnant, but also to protect you from a long, long list of sexually transmitted diseases. Be safe.

Dating agencies

A whole industry has sprung up to help couples meet one another.

Dating agencies used to be considered the last chance saloon, and only something that sad, dull, boring people would ever have to resort to. This is clearly complete rubbish, and dating agencies have a huge part to play in bringing people together.

If you really want to meet someone and you've tried all the usual ways (going round the supermarket on a Friday night or joining a car maintenance class), then it is well worth considering a reputable agency. Be careful though, some of these agencies are very exclusive and expensive and the really top-class ones can charge a couple of thousand pounds signing-on fee.

When filling out your application form, keep it short, sweet and *honest*. There's no point in saying you are a willowy blonde on the right side of thirty-five if you are short, dark and fifty-five.

Be very clear about stating what you are looking for, whether it is just a bit of fun or a long-term relationship. If you really couldn't go out with a smoker then put that on the form. You can include hobbies and passions, but make sure you are truthful. If you say you love opera when you really love *soap* opera you could end up with the wrong person altogether. You shouldn't feel you have to impress with your intellect. Telling white lies will backfire when you eventually start going on dates.

After splitting up with her long-term boyfriend over three years ago, and not having so much as a sniff of a man she would have liked to go out for a pizza with (never mind anything more exciting), my friend Liz plucked up courage and joined a dating agency.

She was very nervous on the first date and, although he was a very sweet man, he wasn't someone she wanted to see again.

It was fourth time lucky, however, when she met Mark. He really was her Mr Right and they have been going steady for about four months.

It's early days, but I reckon they are made for each other. The only thing is that they are still a bit uncomfortable about telling people that they met through an agency, and will often mumble something about 'meeting in a pub' whenever anyone asks.

I do think that attitude is changing though and so it should – there are some wonderful happy-ever-after stories of couples of all ages who have found happiness through an agency.

If you do decide to give it a go remember that there will almost certainly be more women on the agency's books than men. There's nothing wrong with being excited and hopeful about finding love through a dating agency, but it might be fairer on yourself just to assume that you could meet some people who might be fun to go out with. Then, if romance blooms, that's a big fat bonus. If you are too hopeful or desperate then I do think you could be doomed to disappointment.

Although the agency will vet everyone who comes in through their doors, the rules about dating someone by this method are still the same as if you'd met them any other way – Be Safe.

Speed dating

This is a fairly new phenomenon which started (where else) in the States – it's the dating equivalent of a McDonald's hamburger, a sort of 'Macdate' – and which sprang out of the premise that within three minutes you know whether or not the person who you are on a date with is going to float your boat. It's designed for people who don't have a lot of time, but who do want to meet someone they might be able to have a relationship with.

What usually happens is that you go along to the venue (usually a private room in a bar or restaurant), and when you arrive you are given a scorecard, a pen and a badge. You sit and talk to someone for three minutes, then a buzzer will be sounded and you all change places. After each three minutes, you mark on the scorecard whether or not you want to see this person again.

If you tick four boxes and two of the same people tick your box – then you have two matches. Usually you contact each other via e-mail and then it's down to you.

I'm not sure whether three minutes really is enough time to decide whether or not you want to see someone again. You would only be going by physical appearance because it would be impossible to get to know enough about people in such a short time – especially if they were a bit nervous about the whole thing.

It is also a symptom of a very modern syndrome where women and men run through loads of dates and discard people very quickly because they 'might meet someone better'. I believe they are very likely to end up alone.

So, I have my doubts about speed dating. It is yet another option for those wanting to meet new people, but it's far healthier if you go with the idea of broadening your social circle rather than finding your soul mate.

If it goes well

Let's assume that your first date goes well, and you have established that he seems a kind, decent bloke who makes you laugh and whose company you enjoy.

Take it easy, don't try too hard, and once again *be yourself!* He is probably just as nervous as you are.

If you are very lucky he'll be someone who will listen to what you have to say and be genuinely interested in what's going on in your life. (If only men realised how attractive being a good listener really is, they would have much more success with women.)

I think there is a lot of truth in the old saying that when you are really looking for something you won't find it, and when you're not looking you will. Just don't give up hope, and remember that everyone who is looking for love feels exactly the same as you do. As a last resort, you could always move to Alaska, where single men outnumber women ten to one. It should be pointed out that while the odds are good, the goods are odd.

Lorraine's Lifelines

- It's fine to have high standards – but don't dismiss someone just because he doesn't fit your ideal of the perfect partner.
- When dating on the Internet or from lonely hearts' adverts – be careful.
- Don't get drunk – even if you are nervous.
- Dating agencies can work – but make sure it is a bona fide organisation.
- *Enjoy* yourself out there but always be safe.

HOW TO KEEP LOVE ALIVE

My mum married my dad when she was just seventeen. Over forty years later they are still together. They've had some tough times, but they are from the generation that believes they have made a commitment to each other and should stick together through thick and thin, until death us do part.

Times have changed and one in three marriages now ends in divorce. Things are different now: women are no longer as dependent financially on men, and there's not the stigma there was about a broken marriage.

I think we've gone too far the other way and made it too easy and too acceptable for couples to give up on each other and on their relationship. Obviously, when someone is in an abusive relationship and they are either being physically or mentally hurt and demeaned, my advice would always be to get out, to get out now and to get out fast. However, I do think that when two people love each other, and especially if they have kids, they should try absolutely everything and explore every avenue to stay together. I believe divorce is too easy, and that when some young couples have a blistering row, instead of cooling down and sorting it out they head for the divorce lawyers.

How do you avoid the split?

Looking at people who have successful relationships, it is generally couples who completely trust each other and who give each other space to do their own thing. Yes they enjoy being together, but they are also happy off on their own, spending time with friends and family, or enjoying a hobby or interest. This gives them so much more to talk about and enriches the relationship.

You don't have to be joined at the hip for a relationship to work, and the worst thing you can do is to stifle your partner and stop them from doing what they want to do (within reason – you don't want them attending a swingers' party or dancing around stone circles at midnight).

When a marriage goes stale and the couple become bored with one another, that's when men and women can stray. They are looking for that excitement of a new relationship that makes them feel alive.

George and Irene have been married for twenty-five years and they have just celebrated their silver wedding anniversary.

Earlier this year their eldest child moved into his own flat and the youngest went off to university. All of a sudden George and Irene were alone in the house.

They found, much to their horror, that they actually didn't know each other at all. They were like virtual strangers because for years they had been communicating via the children. Everything centred around the two boys and, now that they were no longer around, the house seemed very empty.

Although George and Irene slept in the same bed, they rarely had sex (initially they didn't want to embarrass the teenagers, but then they had fallen out of the habit), and they had also gotten into the way of simply not talking to each other.

Whatever it was that had made them fall in love with each other had been lost. They'd also been taking each other completely for granted. Irene had a part-time job and was completely wrapped up in the boys, and George had a demanding job that took up all his time and energy. He'd come home, eat his meal and retreat behind his newspaper.

Irene is a friend and she confided in me about the state of her marriage.

She was upset, frustrated and bewildered. She hadn't realised things were so bad until she was left alone with George, and she didn't know what to do.

I told her that she wasn't alone and that many couples are in exactly the same boat – but instead of looking on the negative side, she should treat this as a way to get to know her husband all over again. They loved each other once, and maybe they could rekindle the flames. It was certainly worth a go.

I told her to get him to take her on a 'date', and for both of them to try and make an effort to make love. Also, simply to talk to one another and to see if there was anything actually worth saving, and to pluck up the courage to be honest with one another and say what it was they wanted out of the relationship.

I also told her to get herself a hobby, now that she doesn't have to run after her big lumps of sons, so she decided to learn Spanish and has also joined a painting class. Her paintings are pretty ropey (she admits this herself) but she really enjoys herself, and it gives her something to do, now that she doesn't have to tidy up after two messy teenagers, feed them and run them around in the car.

She's doing a lot more that is just for her and separate from her home life. She's also getting to meet new people and make new friends. Of course she misses her boys, but she is also enjoying a bit of peace and quiet and a tidy house, and they still come and see her at weekends (with a shed load of dirty laundry).

Irene and George have uneasily begun to rebuild bridges. He comes home from work and, instead of disappearing behind his newspaper, he asks his wife about what she's been up to. She takes an interest in what he's been doing, and at least they are talking.

There's no 'happy ever after' to this story, but they are at least trying to save what they have, and doing their best to fix it.

Can you ever get that spark back?

Well, even though you can be restricted by looking after children, by work commitments and by money, you shouldn't lose sight of the fact that you need to work at your marriage, and that you mustn't take each other for granted.

If you have young children, you should try and get some time to yourselves as a couple. Steve and I occasionally meet for lunch on a Friday when Rosie is at school. We get a bit dressed up (I swap my jogging bottoms for cleanish combat trousers) and we have a couple of hours to ourselves. Of course we can do this because I am usually finished work by lunchtime and Steve is a freelance cameraman and works odd hours – but if you can manage one night out together, perhaps even once a fortnight, it will really help.

When you have kids your conversation can consist only of 'It's your turn to take the bin out' and 'We've run out of toilet roll'. It is important to talk to one another about other things in your lives, to discuss possible holidays, or plans for the future, or just to exchange your news. All it takes for you to get some time together is a bit of planning, a good babysitter, and both of you to make the effort.

You don't want to end up with you both looking at each other in complete bewilderment when the kids have flown the nest, wondering 'Who on earth is this person, and how the hell can I spend the rest of my life with them?'

WHEN THINGS GO WRONG

On the surface Tom Cruise and Nicole Kidman had it all.

They are both ridiculously good looking, rich and successful. They seemed wildly in love and they had adopted two children together. When I interviewed Nicole before the split she fizzed with excitement when talking about her husband, and said she still had to pinch herself to believe that he had chosen her out of all the women in the world. By all accounts he was a romantic wooer and a romantic husband. They were living the kind of life that we all think must be completely perfect and wonderful.

As we know now, everything in their garden was not rosy at all. Tom ditched Nicole just before their tenth wedding anniversary, and shortly afterwards began stepping out with Penelope Cruz.

Cracks in the marriage first began showing themselves on the set of the movie they were making together, *Eyes Wide Shut*, the last film directed by Stanley Kubrick. It was a gruelling project for both Tom and Nicole and shooting lasted for the best part of two years. Kubrick was a perfectionist, often shooting the same scene from every conceivable angle, over and over again. It took more than two years to complete and stripped the couple naked both physically and mentally. I think that such a project would put strain on even the strongest marriage.

Nicole dealt with the break-up in a very grown-up way. She was in the middle of promoting the movie *Moulin Rouge* and, although she knew that journalists would be more interested in her break-up than the film, she didn't shirk any interviews and was very mature in answering questions. She was clearly deeply hurt, but she dealt with the collapse of her marriage by coming out with some awesome performances and she never looked more beautiful. However, she has confessed to suffering anxiety attacks in the aftermath of the split which led to her feeling vulnerable and very insecure.

It seems strange that such a beautiful, successful and seemingly confident woman should suffer from nerves, and Nicole has also confessed that she is scared, every time she takes on a role, that she won't be able to do it justice. She has also had to put up with the rumour mill linking her to every leading man (available or otherwise) that she acts alongside.

When you look at photos of Nicole just after the break-up, she looks relieved of a large burden and actually rather happy. Either she is an even better actress than I thought, or she is really saying to Tom Cruise, 'Just look at what you are missing, shorty!' This reminds me of the photo of Princess Diana looking stunning in an amazing, short, low-cut, off-the-shoulder black gown on the same night as Prince

Charles was confessing his adultery on TV. Diana secured every front page the next day and the nation looked at this vibrant, sexy young woman and wondered what on earth Prince Charles was doing. There was a feeling that if Tom and Nicole and Charles and Diana couldn't get it right then what hope is there for the rest of us?

The truth is that marriages and living together need a lot of hard work. Just like a garden that will get untidy and ugly and wither if you neglect it and leave it alone, so it is with relationships. You get out what you put in.

Dealing with betrayal

When your relationship flounders, for whatever reason, it leaves you with a horrible feeling of failure. Especially if you are left for someone else. If you are the one who has been betrayed, then you are in for a hellish time. Many women are angry about knowing their husband or partner has been sleeping with someone else, but it is the whole package of lies and betrayal that hurts the most. As I have said already, I think I could forgive a one-night stand, but a proper relationship with all the deceit that goes with it, I would find very hard to come to terms with.

One of my friends recently discovered her husband was having an affair. His mother was taken seriously ill on a Friday when he said he was at a weekend conference. She called his mobile, but it was switched off, so she phoned his work to find out exactly where he was staying. Of course there was no conference; he was having a dirty weekend with his girlfriend. My friend felt utterly humiliated, betrayed and also very very stupid that she hadn't spotted the signs. She confronted him and they had the mother of all rows, which ended in her telling him to get out and him hitting the bottle.

When they had stopped screaming at one another, and actually started to talk, it became clear that he was bored and unhappy in the marriage. The younger woman made him feel more alive, the sex was exciting and he even rather enjoyed the danger of being caught. It looked on the surface that it was the affair that caused all the problems in this marriage. However, very often infidelity happens because the relationship is already in trouble. My friend and her husband had fallen out of love and had completely stopped talking to one another.

I cannot stress too often how important it is to keep lines of communication open. I know it sounds obvious, but you cannot read each other's minds and you have to talk to each other to know what is working and what isn't.

In some cases, affairs happen because one partner wants out of the relationship, but can't bring themselves to be honest.

Often those who are cheating secretly want to be found out, to have the showdown and then be shown the door. It's a very cowardly way to act and causes much more pain than being honest and straightforward.

I believe that this is what happened in my friend's case. He wanted out – but wasn't brave enough to tell his wife. Having an affair was his way of escaping the relationship.

They have no children and neither of them really wants to stay together. In this case it was best for both of them to split.

When an affair is discovered, and after you have said your piece and (understandably) raged, ranted, cursed and cried, you then have to decide whether or not you want to save your marriage or your relationship.

A betrayal can be overcome, but both parties have to be completely sincere about starting over again. You have to be able to forgive and accept forgiveness, and you have to mean it. There is no point in saying 'I forgive you' when you are secretly seething and will not lose an opportunity to reopen the wound.

If you had no idea that you were being cheated on, you may feel completely stupid and humiliated. You think everyone is laughing at you and that the whole of your relationship, which you thought of as your safe haven and as solid as a rock, is nothing more than a house of sand. It is completely understandable to go to pieces when you are betrayed and lied to – and to feel a burning sense of anger, especially when other people who you thought were your friends knew about the affair. The death of trust is like any bereavement and it hurts like hell. You want to hide yourself away from the world, but you owe it to yourself to fight back.

Jerry Hall forgave and forgave Mick Jagger his many infidelities, but eventually it all got too much for her and she walked away. I am surprised it took this bright, beautiful woman so long to give him the booted foot. He definitely behaved like a horny teenager (while looking like a rutting old goat) throughout their marriage – but Jerry allowed him to get away with it.

I think it suited Hilary Clinton to have her husband behave like the White House was his own personal bordello. It gave her the upper hand and the moral high ground, and I think she chose to turn a blind eye in order to get power – we might just see her in the White House on her own next time round.

Katrina was married for six years and has a small son aged two and a half. She admits that when her baby was born she made him the centre of her world, and that, with hindsight, she probably didn't pay as much attention to her husband as she should have. She was so caught up with being a mother – it was (understandably) the most important thing in her life – that she didn't spot any of the warning signs that should have told her that he was unhappy and feeling shut out. Mind you, he should also have told her that he felt so neglected.

They stopped bothering to communicate. They never really talked about anything apart from what was on the TV and what they were having for dinner.

Katrina put on a lot of weight before and after the baby was born. It was a tough birth and she didn't really want to have sex for a long time afterwards. She also felt fat, frumpy and undesirable. It's not at all uncommon for new mothers to feel this way and it takes a lot of love and understanding by your partner to reassure you that you are still a vibrant sexy woman.

Katrina was devastated when her husband confessed he was seeing someone else, that they were in love and that he was leaving. She had had absolutely no idea at all. She was so wrapped up in being a mum that she had forgotten to be a wife as well. It's not easy trying to be both and she could have done with a lot more help from her husband, but he didn't take well to the responsibility of being a father and to the upheaval in their formerly well-ordered life. The sassy career girl he had married had turned into a tired, overweight housewife and he didn't like it one little bit.

Katrina is now trying to cope as a single mum. She does get maintenance, but it is hard for her financially. However she seems far happier now than when she was trying to struggle to be the perfect mother and wife. Of course, she has to have a relationship with her former husband because of their son, but for them there is no way back. He is living with someone else and he and Katrina have started divorce proceedings.

Talking to both of them it is clear that before they got married they never actually sat down with one another and talked about the really big stuff in life. They never even discussed whether they wanted children. Katrina took it for granted – he wasn't so sure and had reservations, but he never discussed them with her.

Top of the list of things to be talked about before marriage is whether or not to have children, and although you cannot order them up like pizzas, you should have the conversation about whether you both actually want to be parents or not. Then you have to talk about plans for the future. Are you both happy in your jobs? Does he have a desire to give it all up and retire to Australia or Spain? So many couples get confetti in their eyes and don't actually see past the wedding ceremony to what life will be like afterwards. Then they wonder why they have married someone who seems to be a complete stranger, who wants different things. No wonder the marriage breaks down as one, or both partners run into the arms of someone else.

Just because you have been let down once, don't believe it will automatically happen again. Don't assume that all men are rats who will cheat on you. It will sour your relationship with every single male you come into contact with – whether you have a proper relationship with them or not.

Try and learn from your bad experiences and don't fall into the trap of repeating your mistakes over and over again.

Lorraine's Lifelines

- Talk to each other.
- Never take one another for granted.
- Be honest with each other.
- Try everything you can to save your relationship, if that's what you both want.
- Do not be bitter – you are only going to harm yourself.
- Don't assume that this will happen to you again – or it just might.

Separation and divorce

If you have tried everything and there's nothing to save from your marriage, then the next step is separation and divorce.

If there are no children involved, it's relatively straight-forward, but no divorce is ever going to be easy.

One of my friends who got divorced two years ago, after putting up with her husband's affairs for the best part of a decade, told me that the best bit of advice she was ever given, after finally deciding to kick him out, was to go and get her hair cut at the most expensive salon she could afford. I thought this was a rather trivial thing to do when your whole world was tumbling down around your ears, but she said that going to have her hair cut short, highlighted and in a completely new style, gave her a real confidence boost at a time when her self-esteem was at an all time low.

After stepping out of the salon she went and bought herself some new make-up and a new outfit and, although she couldn't really afford it, she felt ten times better for having spent some time and money on herself.

Of course a new hair-do is a bit like putting a sticking plaster on an amputation – and when you split up from someone it does feel as if an important part of yourself has been cut off. Divorce might be a lot more common now than it ever was, but in all but a few circumstances it is painful, messy and traumatic. Be aware that no matter how much you want to get divorced, a part of you will be grieving for the death of your marriage. it is also natural to feel a sense of failure and to feel very down. I know they sell Happy Divorce cards in the shops these days, but, with some exceptions (for example women in a violent marriage), I don't think all that many couples ever really feel like celebrating.

DEALING WITH THE TOUGH STUFF

We all go through tough times in our lives. We may have to deal with nasty people, or our kids being bullied at school, or a violent relationship, or feeling depressed. We will certainly have to deal with the death of someone we love. It's often not fair, but it is part of life, and there are ways to deal with even the darkest days.

Difficult neighbours

Nasty neighbours can make your life hell. When I was working for TVam, I had a couple who lived in the flat below me who must have worked in a night club, because I would hear their door opening and banging shut at four in the morning and then a blast of loud music and usually a lot of giggling or arguing, depending on how their evening had gone. It wasn't a problem for me, because I needed to be out of the house at 4.15 a.m. and I looked upon them as my back-up alarm clock, but if I had been doing a regular nine to five job, they would have driven me insane.

Noisy, difficult and aggressive neighbours are insufferable, especially those who play music loudly, do DIY in the middle of the night, or allow their dog to bark constantly. It's all about having consideration for others and treating people the way you would like to be treated yourself. Some people are appallingly selfish, and if you happen to live next door to one of these monsters then you have my sympathy.

HOW DO YOU DEAL WITH IT?

I know it is stating the obvious, but you have to talk to your neighbours and let them know you're unhappy. Being reticent Brits and not wanting to make a fuss, we always wait too long before complaining. This means that by the time you do speak up and make your feelings known, you are a seething pent-up volcano of emotions and things can get out of hand.

The best thing to do is to ask your neighbours in the

nicest possible way if they wouldn't mind turning down Eminem because it is late and you have to get up for work the next morning, or point out gently that maybe mowing the lawn at midnight is a bit anti-social. Be reasonable and be calm. If you go to see them and you are aggressive and angry (no matter how justified) you will get nowhere.

You can hope that they will invite you in for a cup of tea and a chat, and you can sort it all out over a Hob Nob. However, in some cases, it is more likely that they will get the hump and you could have the beginnings of a very nasty little war.

If you really do feel that you cannot talk to your neighbour – maybe you hate confrontation, or maybe they are a bit scary – then write down your concerns in a letter and send it to them.

If they respond with little more than a f**k off then you have two choices. You can put up with it, or you can take it further.

If you are in rented accommodation, get in touch with the landlord. If you are in a council house, contact your local housing officer, but whatever your circumstances you can complain to the environmental health department and they could serve a Noise Abatement Order. If your neighbours refuse to comply with this, for whatever reason, you can take legal action, but this is a last resort. Once lawyers get involved there's no going back, and it's hard to live next door to someone once you have eyeballed each other from opposite sides of a courtroom.

You should keep a diary of their anti-social behaviour, and any correspondence, and enlist the help of other neighbours who might also be disturbed. Some councils offer a mediation service where you can all sit down and talk over the complaints.

Helen and Jim used to love their house on a small estate until, in May 2002, the family from hell moved in next door.

The husband and wife screamed abuse at each other, drank heavily and let their five kids, aged eight to fifteen, do more or less what they liked. The garden quickly became overgrown and usually had car parts strewn across the front lawn. They played their TV so loud that Helen and Jim couldn't hear their own programmes, and at weekends the children stayed up to the wee small hours arguing, screaming and playing records so loud that ornaments in Helen's living room would dance about on the mantelpiece. There were also two massive Alsatian dogs that barked constantly and Helen was terrified of them.

Helen and Jim tried to talk to their neighbours but were given short shrift. They kept detailed records and complained to the housing authority. Meanwhile they were both utterly miserable. Helen said that even when

it was reasonably quiet they would both lie in bed rigid with tension, waiting for the noise to start up. A combination of lack of sleep, stress and misery made them both ill. Helen says she would rather have lived next door to the Addams family.

The situation was only resolved when the husband moved out after a series of blistering rows. Helen found it much easier to talk to the wife, and with him out of the picture there was less fighting and tension.

The family certainly haven't turned into the Waltons, and still make an intolerable amount of noise, but the dogs have gone to another relative (probably one of the kids tried to bite them) and things have settled down a lot.

If, however, the husband comes back, it is likely to flare up again and Helen and Jim are seriously thinking of moving away.

Remember, though, that it doesn't always have to end with the removal van at your front door.

The solution, as with so many things, could lie in trying to communicate better.

My friend Jackie had a young family move in next door and she found them extremely noisy compared to the old couple who used to live there. The children, young boys of eight and eleven, were in the back garden a lot and their games were pretty loud.

Jackie seethed and fumed for about two weeks before finally going round and 'having a word'. Luckily, she kept calm and was met by an extremely nice but very harassed young mum who was very apologetic and promised that the boys would be quieter, especially after 6 p.m. when Jackie got back from work, but she did say that they are kids and couldn't be expected to creep around like timid white mice.

Jackie realised that she had a point. The boys weren't tearaways, but perfectly normal kids letting off steam and playing games. It was just that the contrast between their level of noise and the old couple's was so marked.

They have come to a compromise and, although Jackie still gets annoyed when she is trying to read a book in the garden and the boys are playing football, she knows that her neighbours aren't deliberately trying to antagonise her and she often hears their mum telling them to keep the noise down.

It's all about doing as you would be done by and having a bit of consideration for one another.

- If your neighbours are driving you crazy, try and talk to them calmly.
- Write down all the instances where you feel they have behaved unreasonably.
- Contact your landlord or the local council.
- Try not to let the situation blight your life.
- Going to court should always be a last resort.

Bullying

Almost all of us will experience bullying at some time in our lives. It could be at home by our sisters and brothers, or during our schooldays, or at work by our boss.

I was bullied at school, for no other reason than I was reasonably bright and accused of being the 'teacher's pet'. The fact that my mum put my hair in ringlets didn't help. It was a thoroughly miserable time and I used to dread school break times. It didn't last all that long, and it was soon someone else's turn to be picked on, but I remember not wanting to go to school, and faking tummy aches and head aches so I could stay off and be safe at home with my mum.

In those days, bullying was not taken as seriously as it is now and it tended to be thought of as part of the rough and tumble of growing up. When bullies were caught in the act they were given the strap (This was a thick leather belt which teachers used to thump you with on your poor trembling upturned hands. I had my share of the strap, usually for talking in the classroom, and it stung like hell.) Hitting kids for hitting kids doesn't exactly get to the root of the problem.

Bullying is a horrible thing to have to cope with and I don't for one minute subscribe to the old-fashioned theory that it is in any way character building or that being bullied at school means you will be able to deal with life's knocks. It makes you scared and eats away at your confidence.

At least sixteen children in Britain kill themselves every year, directly as a result of being bullied. Can you imagine how bad things must have become for those poor little souls for them to consider suicide as the only way out of their hell, and the devastation of their parents and loved ones left to cope with such a waste of a young life, and all the feelings of guilt and helplessness?

In July 2001, Laura Grimes killed herself. She was only fourteen, and had been looking forward to being a bridesmaid at her sister's wedding, but she left letters describing how her life became unbearable when she became physically and verbally bullied: 'Don't worry about me. I have gone up above where I really want to be. No bullies, no school, just happiness.' She also pleaded with the bullies not to pick on anyone else.

In November 2001, Elaine Swift died after swallowing over 100 paracetamol tablets. Despite performing a liver transplant, surgeons were unable to save the sixteen-year-old from Hartlepool. Elaine had previously become a local heroine after donating bone marrow to save her younger sister's life. Her father believes that the attention she received from the local media at the time caused resentment, and that his daughter was bullied to death.

IF YOUR CHILD IS BEING BULLIED AT SCHOOL

These days most schools have an anti-bullying policy, but you first have to establish whether or not your child is being bullied, and if so just how serious it is.

Look out for those sore heads and sore tummies on school mornings, and if your child is a bit quieter than usual. If they are coming home with scratches and bruises or have 'lost' money or possessions, or their schoolwork has dramatically worsened, then they may well be being bullied.

You must try and create an atmosphere where your child feels safe and able to talk to you. You could gently ask them about school bullies and whether or not it has ever happened to them, but it might be hard to coax the information out of them. Very often children feel ashamed to tell their parents they are being bullied. They think that the parents will be cross that they have somehow let them down.

Be patient, but if you are convinced they are being bullied you must get them to talk to you about it. Many children feel embarrassed or feel weak by admitting they are being bullied. You must make it clear that you don't think any less of them for being bullied, and in fact you are so proud of them for telling you the truth.

You have to take their fears seriously, but please try not to over-react. Of course you will be angry and upset that your child is having such a rough time. If you yourself were bullied at school, seeing your child go through the same kind of suffering you did will be doubly hard to bear, and could bring all sorts of bad memories back. I wouldn't blame you at all for wanting to go and give the little buggers responsible a thick ear. Of course *you can't, you won't*, and *you never, ever should*, but it doesn't stop part of you wanting to.

Be calm and tell your child you will do your best to sort it out. Your child will be feeling very vulnerable, so give him or her a big hug and lots of reassurance. Just talking about the bullying can be a big help, but you have to make a child who is being bullied know that you are on their side and you love them very much.

It's worth talking to your child about why some people act like bullies. Maybe you can use examples of baddies in their favourite cartoons who get their comeuppance (the wicked stepmother and the ugly sisters in *Cinderella*, or Captain Hook in *Peter Pan*).

Be supportive; let your child know he or she can confide in you at any time, and that you will help them to tackle the problem.

HOW CAN YOU HELP YOUR CHILD DEAL WITH A BULLY?

If a child is being bullied there really is no point in fighting fire with fire. Violence and anger just make the problem worse, and someone could get seriously hurt.

If the bullying is taking the form of teasing and name calling then you should tell your child to say in a clear voice, 'I don't like the way you are treating me and I want you to stop it.' Then your child should walk away.

Physical bullying is more serious and can be in the form of kicking, hitting, hair pulling, pinching and biting. It's scary and it should never be tolerated. This is when you need to enlist the help of the school.

You should talk to your child's teacher and let them know

that your child is being picked on. It is important to let them know *calmly* what is going on, and that you want something done about it. It's worth putting your fears and concerns in writing. Also, ask the head teacher about their anti-bullying policy, and whether or not it has been effective.

Some children just have victim written all over them. Maybe they are shy, or they are physically weak. Maybe they have to wear glasses, or they have red hair, or they have sticky out ears or teeth. The bully will pounce on any excuse to make their lives hell, and the rest of the pack will often follow their lead.

Sometimes they pick on the least confident child who may not have made any friends. If your child is painfully shy you can try and help them. Strike up a friendship with other mums, and take turns to have the children at each others' houses to play, or for tea.

Cheer your child up by telling them about other people who have been bullied at school, but have come successfully through it, including Kate Winslet, Gareth Gates, Tom Cruise and my friend and colleague weather presenter Andrea McLean.

WHAT IF YOUR CHILD IS THE BULLY?

The bully has to be someone's child, and despite all the heartbreak that comes with having a child who is picked on and whose schooldays have become miserable, just think how much worse you would feel if your child was the one doing the bullying. This is much tougher to deal with.

There are many reasons why a child turns into a bully. Bullies are often children who feel inadequate (maybe they aren't finding their lessons as easy as the other kids). They may have a tough home life. Maybe their parents are going through an acrimonious divorce. Some of those big tough bullies in school might be the scared victims at home. Those children who are abused by their parents, or those who are supposed to be caring for them, can often turn out to be the very worst kind of bullies. They really don't know any better, and seem to have an unerring sense of picking on the child who won't or can't fight back.

I know a teacher who had a real problem with a bully in her class. Lots of parents were complaining about this particular child and she had to call the parents in for a meeting. They were shocked that their son was behaving so badly, hitting smaller children and demanding their toys and pocket money. The father became very angry and said that when he got his son home he would give him the thrashing of his life. That's when the teacher realised that it was hardly surprising this kid had become a bully. He had learned all his techniques directly from his aggressive father. Often, bullies know through experience how to make their victims suffer because they have been at the other end of a booted foot at home.

Of course not all bullies come from violent homes, and there's a lot parents and teachers can do to help them change their behaviour. You have to get them to talk to you and you have to encourage them to break their bad bullying habits. Let the school know you are aware of the problems and you are doing your very best to sort it out.

- If you suspect your child is being bullied sit down and talk to him or her about it.
- Don't get angry and upset.
- Don't over-react or try to deal with the bully in an aggressive way yourself.
- Be patient and gentle with your child and reassure them with lots of love and cuddles.
- Talk to the teachers and ask them about their anti-bullying programme.
- If your child is the bully, talk to them and find out why.
- Could your behaviour be a factor?
- Assure the school you are trying to sort it out.

Sadly, the classroom bully often grows up into the board-room bully or the foreman who picks on the weaker members of his workforce. The bad news is that bullying doesn't stop at the end of your school life.

BEING BULLIED IN THE WORKPLACE

I always remember reading *A Christmas Carol* by Charles Dickens, and watching the musical *Scrooge* adapted from it, when the ghost of Christmas Past takes Scrooge back in time to when he was a young apprentice working for Mr Fezziwig. The old gentleman is a wonderful optimist who wants everyone to have a fabulous time and to enjoy life to its fullest, so he throws a Christmas party for everyone. When Scrooge watches them all having fun he tells the ghost that Fezziwig is a truly wonderful man. The ghost says what's so wonderful about spending a few pounds on a party?

Scrooge replies that Fezziwig had the *power* to make his working life happy or miserable, and because he was a good and generous boss, Scrooge and the other workers were happy too. Seeing his old boss makes Scrooge wish he had treated the long suffering Bob Cratchit a bit better.

Sadly, most bosses aren't going to be visited by three ghosts on Christmas Eve to make them turn into wonderfully warm-spirited, generous human beings. Bullying in the workforce is all about that abuse of *power*.

However, bullying is not a sign of strength; it's a sign of weakness. Victimising others is the way the bully hides his (or her) insecurities and inadequacies.

It can take many forms, but the result is that the person being bullied is miserable and can suffer stress-related illnesses.

Bullying can be subtle too. Bullies can undermine confidence and also take credit for other people's hard work. The smiling bully is the hardest one to deal with because you just can't pin them down.

I came upon this definition of bullying in the workplace: 'Bullying is being constantly criticised, belittled, humiliated, threatened or verbally abused. In the work environment it can also mean being excluded or being overloaded with work. It can be the fabricating or twisting of things you have said, taking credit for your ideas or achievements, refusing to allow training or blocking promotion.'

That just about sums up what goes on in some work-places, but it doesn't describe the sheer stomach-churning, heart-sinking-to-your-boots sense of being the workplace whipping boy. Very few people can just walk out on their job, and the bully will be well aware of the responsibilities the person he is picking on will have.

While it is easy to rationalise bullying, the consequences of such behaviour can be tragic.

In November 1999 a young man, Jermaine Lee, who worked in the Royal Mail in Birmingham, hanged himself. Before taking his own life, he wrote a note to his mother saying 'They have won.' His suicide note went on, 'I love you. I always have and I always will. I never wanted to go like this but it's the only way out. Those guys at work hate me.'

His shocked parents wanted to get to the bottom of something that made their son so depressed and in such despair that he killed himself. After an investigation, the Royal Mail discovered that Jermaine had been the victim of bullying and harassment by his fellow workers. His mother was told that there was a climate of fear, bullying and racism and although Jermaine had complained nothing had been done. He had suffered for years.

Jermaine's family were given £100,000 compensation and the Royal Mail introduced fifty recommendations to change the way they deal with bullying and racism in the workforce.

Of course this was all too late for Jermaine.

So how *do* you deal with the bullying of the office ogre?

You can be passive and ignore it completely, hoping it will go away. This might work in the long run, but it will take a long time for your tormentor to lose interest – and even if he does, he will only start picking on some other poor soul.

Your best plan is to have plenty of ammunition. Keep a record of any incidents when you have been bullied and take a note of the names of any potential witnesses.

You should try and be more assertive. I know it doesn't come easy, but sometimes, if you calmly and quietly tell the bully that you will not put up with their unfair and inappropriate behaviour, then they might just back down. Remember, most bullies are full of hot air, and if you stand up to them they quickly deflate. It is worth a try.

If you are being bullied, make sure you talk to someone. If you feel you can't talk to your partner, then try and unload some of this burden on to a friend or someone at work. If the situation gets too much for you, contact your Personnel/Human Resources department. They are there to help you, and if they are good at their job they will have an anti-bullying policy in operation.

Lorraine's Lifelines

- Try and be assertive but if that doesn't work then:
- Keep a record of any incidents of bullying.
- Get help from the Human Resources or Personnel department.
- Don't just lower your head and accept the situation.
- No one deserves to be bullied and you must try and do something about it.

Domestic violence

Once upon a time domestic violence happened behind closed doors and no one (least of all the victims) ever talked about it. Women (and men, because they get battered too) would mutter some excuse about falling down the stairs or hitting their head on a cupboard door. They were ashamed, scared, and often trapped by lack of money or by having nowhere they could go to escape.

Things have changed, and in particular, in 2002/3, the *Eastenders* storyline of Little Mo and Trevor really struck a chord and helped so many people in violent relationships.

Both of the actors, Kacey Ainsworth and Alex Ferns, were very aware of how much responsibility their portrayal of these characters carried. They had to get it right and make sure that the relationship was convincing. The result was not only a powerful piece of drama, but the chance to bring the whole subject out into the open. Women who were being battered *and* violent husbands were encouraged to seek help.

Domestic violence is being treated much more seriously these days and the options for women who want to escape from terror and fear are much better – but we still have a long way to go.

If you are in a violent relationship, do not allow yourself to get hurt any longer, especially if you have children. You are worth so much more than that, and you should not have to live in fear. If your partner won't agree to get help, you have to get yourself out of there.

REAL LIFE SOLUTIONS

Everyone envied Louise her handsome, caring considerate husband. He treated her like a princess, he did his share of the domestic chores and everyone thought they were the ideal couple.

What they didn't know was that he regularly used her as a punchbag and made her life a complete and utter misery. It was like living with Jekyll and Hyde. To the world outside he was Mr Wonderful, but on his own with Louise he was a monster.

It didn't take much to trigger one of his rages. It could be that he had had a bad day at the office, or he didn't like his meal, or maybe he thought she was being a nag about something. She never really knew when he would erupt, and so she walked on egg shells all the time.

She was too proud and ashamed to tell anyone what she thought was her 'dirty secret', but when he broke her nose for no real reason in particular, she knew it was time to get out.

Sadly, many of her former friends and her in-laws blame her for the split and have stood by her ex-husband. He is such a convincing charmer he has made them believe Louise was a nightmare to live with and was making it all up.

Apart from the injuries to her hand and nose, she sustained countless bruises and cuts over the years as well as being subjected to torrents of abuse. He told her she was fat, ugly and useless and no man would look at her twice, that she was hopeless in bed, a useless cook and an appalling mother. Unfortunately, the only time she went to the hospital was for her broken nose, and she didn't press charges, so there's no record of his violence.

One of the reasons she stayed so long was that she didn't have any money of her own, but mainly it was because she did actually love him. He managed to kick that out of her, but she really did believe for a while that it was mostly her fault and that she drove him to violence. It's only now that she is away from him that she can see things the way they really are.

Louise was lucky. She went back to her parents who live hundreds of miles away, and they have given her a place to stay. She is now trying to find work and rebuild her life. She has had a lot of help from Women's Aid and from meeting other women in the same situation.

Rape and assault

If this has happened to you, I am sincerely sorry. It is a horrific abuse of power, an appalling violation and a very tough thing to overcome. However, there's a lot of help and support out there and you are not alone.

Remember that everyone reacts in a different way. You might be too shocked to cry or you might not be able to stop sobbing, but you should tell the police, and if you have been injured, you must get medical attention right away. Your instinct is to get into a bath and scrub away the hurt and this is completely understandable. However, if you want the person who did this to you to be caught you need to wait until you have been examined because the police need forensic evidence. For the same reason, keep the clothes you were wearing.

If you go to the police be assured that their methods when dealing with someone who has been raped or seriously sexually assaulted are very different these days. You should be treated sympathetically and gently. You will almost certainly be examined by a female doctor and interviewed by specially trained female officers. They will talk you through the procedure and what will happen if you decide to press charges. This is completely your decision.

You will need a thorough health check to make sure you aren't pregnant or have caught any sexually transmitted diseases – a ghastly side-effect of a horrible crime, but you must get the all clear for your own peace of mind.

The majority of women who are raped know their attacker, and so it might not be possible to confide in your partner, your friends or your family. If you cannot talk to them, then call a rape helpline. In all cases, it really is vital that you talk about what happened and don't bottle it all up inside. Just being able to tell someone 'I've been raped' is a big step towards your recovery. A really good way of coming to terms with what has happened and moving on is to talk to other women who have been through similar experiences. It won't be easy but you can get through it.

Depression

We have all had times in our lives when we have felt really down. It might be because we feel a bit ill, or things aren't going too well at work or with a relationship. It could just be because it's November and it's cold, dark and wet. Usually we snap out of it after a couple of days, and it helps to talk things out with a friend.

Depression is quite a different beast altogether. It can last for months and symptoms usually include some or all of the following:

- Feeling downright unhappy and miserable most of the time (although the feelings might lift a bit sometimes).
- Being unable to see the joy in anything.
- Generally losing interest in life.
- Not being able to cope with things the way you used to.

- Loss of appetite.
- Having trouble sleeping.
- Losing interest in sex.
- Feeling completely exhausted and weary all the time.
- Avoiding other people.
- Losing your self-confidence.
- Having suicidal thoughts.

Sometimes depression can come up behind you very slowly and gradually like a thick black cloud. You might not realise at first just how downright rotten you feel, and you might even forget what it was like to feel completely well. Being exhausted all the time wears you down and then, if you aren't getting to sleep, or not sleeping well, you wake up feeling more tired than when you went to bed and the whole thing becomes a downward spiral.

SO WHY AM I SO DEPRESSED?

There are many, many reasons. Sometimes people who are depressed can't actually put their finger on why they feel so bad, and this is as depressing for the sufferer as it is for the people around them. It could be something understandable like a bereavement, or divorce, or losing your job. Of course you will feel low trying to cope with your grief or your disappointment, but these feelings usually diminish sufficiently so that you can try and get back to some kind of normality. Depression, however, persists.

Depression can happen if you aren't able to cope well with an upheaval or distressing event in your life. It can also happen when someone has no one to talk to and they are feeling lonely, or if they are seriously ill, especially if it is an illness that takes a long time to recover from.

Booze makes you depressed. I can't drink gin without coming over all maudlin, and if you are a real drinker then you will more than likely wake up in the morning feeling hung over as well as depressed and that is not a good combination. With booze it is a bit like the chicken and the egg. What comes first, the depression or the alcohol to numb the pain? Was it drinking too much that made you depressed?

Some people may be predisposed to depression and it could run in the family, but not always, so if you do have a parent with serious depression, it doesn't mean it will happen to you.

We are pretty appalling in this country at dealing with any kind of mental illness. If someone has a broken arm, we are sympathetic, but a broken mind either means people don't want to discuss it at all or they tell the sufferer to 'Pull themselves together.' This is just about the worst thing you could say to anyone suffering with depression. If they could pull themselves together they would, but not being a pair of curtains, they simply cannot.

Please don't think that depression is some kind of weakness or character flaw. Anyone can become depressed, even the most successful, high achievers who look like they have the world in the palm of their hands.

If you have suffered from depression you are certainly not alone (one in five people in Britain will suffer from some form of depression at some point in their lives) and you are in exalted company. Ex-Spice Girl Melanie

C, Spike Milligan, Virginia Woolf, Vincent Van Gogh, Winston Churchill and Buzz Aldrin have all had to deal with being depressed. Churchill called it his 'black dog'.

I remember interviewing the actor Rod Steiger, a really flamboyant character who starred in the likes of *On the Waterfront* and *Napoleon*. Rod was hilarious when churning out his Hollywood stories, but he told me how he became angry when asked to audition for a hot-shot new boy-wonder director who asked him whether he would be able to handle doing a Southern accent. Rod puffed out his chest and bellowed in his best thespian tones, 'My dear young man, I won an Oscar for my work in the move *In the Heat of the Night* before you were a glint in your daddy's eye!'

Rod may have become exasperated with the new breed of Hollywood players, but the thing that blighted his life was his battle with depression. He told me that it isn't about feeling a little blue, it's wanting to hide in a dark corner with your head in your hands, howling like a dog and crying like a baby. He is one of the few big stars to admit openly to suffering from mental illness. He was almost at the end of his career and didn't care much what anyone thought about him any more, but it was still brave of him to come out and talk about his depression. By speaking out, he and fellow sufferers make it easier for people to accept depression as a serious illness that needs compassion and understanding.

HELP YOURSELF

Once you face up to the fact that you are depressed there's lots you can do to help yourself through it and out the other side.

Once again I would urge you to talk about how you feel. There's no point in keeping it all to yourself. Tell your friends and family about your state of mind. If you are going through a traumatic time, they will want to help you. People like to feel needed and they don't want to be shut out. Forget all that stiff upper lip stuff. Have a good old cry with your mates and let it all out.

Take care of yourself – eat properly and eat well. I know the temptation when you are feeling really low is to disappear into a bottle of Bacardi and I sympathise, but please, please try and lay off the bevy. Drowning your sorrows doesn't work.

You might want to try St John's Wort, which is an alternative therapy you can buy over the counter, and is said by some to work wonders. Most health shops sell it in a 'one a day' tablet form. However, it is very important that you don't take this without consulting your GP if you are on any other tablets or medicine because it can inhibit or react with them.

There's a wonderful scene in *Crocodile Dundee* at a party in New York where all the socialites are comparing stories about their 'shrinks'. A bemused Mick Dundee wonders aloud what this is all about. 'Haven't they any mates?' he demands.

GETTING PROFESSIONAL HELP

While I sympathise with Mick, and I think that friends are people who keep you sane, I also believe that a lot of people with depression need more than the support of friends and family – although that is clearly an enormous bonus on the road to recovery. Sometimes you do have to call in the professionals, and the most important thing is not to feel ashamed or in any way a 'failure' because you have to see a psychiatrist. If you have a defective bowel, you would go to a person who specialises in that particular area – so why not go to a specialist if your mind isn't functioning properly?

As always, the starting point is your GP who should be

able to refer you to an expert. You may be prescribed anti-depressants and these can help in the short-term, although they should not be used as an alternative to good old-fashioned commonsense advice from your counsellor. Obviously it depends how serious your condition is – some people will need more medication for longer, everyone is different.

If you choose not to get any help for your depression, you might get over it, but the chances are it will rear its ugly head again, maybe even a couple of years down the line.

You wouldn't put up with toothache, so don't put up with a sore mind.

Lorraine's Lifelines

- Recognise the difference between just feeling blue and feeling depressed.
- Talk about your feelings.
- Take care of yourself.
- Lay off the booze.
- Don't think you have failed.
- Don't try to soldier on.
- Don't be ashamed to seek expert advice.

Postnatal depression

Most women get the 'baby blues' in the first week or so after giving birth. I certainly felt a bit overwhelmed and teary. It didn't last and it is very normal, but if these feelings worsen and persist you could have postnatal depression and you'll need help.

Most women find this very difficult to handle. There they are with their longed-for healthy baby, everything should be wonderful – but they feel they simply can't cope.

Denise Welsh who played Natalie in *Coronation Street* came on my TV show in 2001 and admitted that she had suffered appalling postnatal depression after the birth of her first child. The interview created an enormous reaction, with so many sufferers wanting to thank Denise for making them realise that even a woman who seemingly 'had it all' could suffer from that horrible black pit of despair that is the reality of clinical depression. Denise really struggled with coping as a mother, and it nearly put her off having any more kids. Luckily she went on to have another child at the age of forty-three, and after an early health scare baby Louis is thriving, and her PND hasn't come back.

The symptoms of PND are similar to general depression and sufferers feel exhausted, hopeless and often panicky, bursting into tears and feeling frustrated and hopeless. Often everyone's attention is on the new-born baby, which is understandable, but it can mean that the mother gets overlooked.

All new mothers look completely knackered and don't

get enough sleep, but if this is going on for months and goes hand in hand with an inability to cope with simple tasks, mood swings and a lack of interest in everything – then you should get help.

Don't think you are a bad mum if you feel low. It's not your fault you feel so rotten, and people around you should understand that. Don't try and 'soldier on'. If you need help with the baby and you are feeling overwhelmed then don't be embarrassed or ashamed to say you could do with a bit of support. If you feel you can't talk to friends or family, talk to your health visitor. If she's good at her job, she'll probably be able to spot the signs, but no one is going to give you a black mark on your homework book.

There are some ways you can help yourself. Look after yourself. Try and eat properly and sleep when your baby sleeps. Don't use their nap time to do the tidying up. Leave it for someone else to do and have a snooze.

Learn to delegate. If there is a man around, give him things to do. Share the household tasks and the fun bits, like bathing your baby and playing with her.

Let friends help you – don't be a martyr. Give them washing and ironing to do, get them to Hoover, dust and tidy up. Send them to the shops for biscuits, newspaper, tea and chocolate and any other necessities of life you can think of. Most people will be glad to help.

If you have people in your life who criticise you and make you feel that you aren't doing a good job – don't let them through the door. It might be a relative, a neighbour or a so-called friend – if they make you feel bad, you shouldn't feel you have to see them. Only surround yourself with supportive people who understand that you are going through a bad time and will be sympathetic, non-judgemental and will give you a cuddle.

It's a really good idea to talk to other mothers. Try and join a group, or meet up with women you have met at your ante-natal classes. Your health visitor should have details.

Try and have some time to yourself if you can – even if it is only half an hour in front of the TV watching Corrie re-runs.

If all of this doesn't help, then your GP can prescribe medication, counselling, group therapy and support groups. Anti-depressants should only be used in the short term, and only if given by your GP.

It would help enormously if health professionals gave you more warning about PND just so you'd know what signs to look out for.

BEREAVEMENT

Have you ever crossed the street to avoid someone who has recently had a death in the family? Have you wanted to go and pay your respects, but just didn't know what to say? Don't feel too bad about it because you are not alone. As a nation we are generally pretty hopeless when it comes to dealing with death. I think it is partly due to the fact that nowadays few of us die in our beds at home surrounded by our loved ones. Death tends to happen in hospitals and is taken out of our hands.

Often we just don't know what to say to someone who has lost a loved one. It's all right to feel like that – you don't have to have special or magic words to say to someone who is racked with grief. Just telling them how sorry you are and giving them a hug will be much appreciated. Also, just being there to listen to them is so important.

Remember that there is no timetable for grief. Most people never get over their loss, they just learn how to live with it.

My own experiences of death have been mainly through the job that I do. I reported on the Lockerbie disaster, when bodies fell out of the sky, and it was horrific, but it was so outside my experience that it seemed unreal. In fact I think the only way anyone at the scene was able to function was because we all felt we were on a film set.

All I had to do was report on the tragedy, but there were people there who had lost relatives and friends in the most appalling circumstances, and there were also those on the ground who had to deal with the carnage.

We arrived there very quickly – a matter of hours had passed since the plane crashed. I remember how quiet it was that night, and the smell of the aviation fuel. There were small isolated fires everywhere and it looked like the kind of scene you would expect at the end of the world.

There were so many ambulances and rescue workers, but they could not do the job they were trained for because everyone was dead. They were the ones who had to see close-up the kind of sights that no human being should ever have to witness. I don't know how they did it, but they carried out their work with dignity, respect and true courage.

It happened just before Christmas and I remember everyone in the town taking down their decorations, because obviously no one felt like celebrating. On Christmas morning I did my report from the town, and then my dad came down to pick me up and take me back home.

Although I had been surrounded by fellow journalists, I hadn't really had time to reflect on the sheer evilness of those responsible for such an act, or on those people who had died in the sky and on the ground in Lockerbie. I remember all during that two-hour car journey back to my parents' house I just gabbled non-stop about what I had seen and the sheer horror of it all. My dad did exactly the right thing. He listened. All I needed was to pour it all out and it helped a lot.

I don't know how those who lost people they loved and cared deeply about managed to get over such a terrible tragedy. I don't suppose some of them ever will. You just learn to live with loss and take each day as it comes.

Apart from Lockerbie, I didn't actually see a dead body in a coffin until I was thirty-eight and it was under the most heartbreaking of circumstances. I don't need to remind you of what happened on 13 March 1996, when sixteen children and their teacher were gunned down and murdered in Dunblane.

I was listening to the radio when I heard the news, and thought it was all some kind of ghastly mistake. I know Dunblane well. It is a beautiful, quiet town, the kind of place you would move to if you wanted your children to be safe and to thrive. It was unimaginable that something so evil could happen there, and to innocent children and their teachers.

Eamonn Holmes and I did a programme from outside Dunblane cathedral the morning after the murders. The whole country was in shock and I remember we had no scripts or any clear idea of the format of the show, we just went on the air and spoke as two parents would, and tried somehow to reflect the feelings people were experiencing.

I didn't know it at the time, but one of those watching the broadcast was Pam Ross, whose daughter Joanna was one of the children who was so brutally killed. Pam, who has since become a good friend, asked if I would come and see her. I think she just needed to talk to someone about what she was going through, and sometimes it is easier to talk to a stranger.

I will be honest with you, I was very nervous about going to her house, but I also felt very privileged that she had asked me, because she had watched me on TV and read articles I'd written for newspapers and she felt she could relate to me. As soon as I walked through the door I felt as though I had known her all my life. Obviously everyone was shattered by what had happened and we talked and talked for hours. Pam showed me photographs of Joanna who was a heartbreakingly beautiful child with laughter in her eyes and a smile that could melt the hardest heart. Pam's other daughter Alison was still a babe in arms, and I think having her there helped Pam an awful lot. The little girl still needed to be fed and changed and cared for, and was a living example that life does go on, even in the depths of utter despair.

When we had drunk about fifteen cups of tea, Pam asked me if I wanted to see Joanna. I had had no idea that the little angel was upstairs in her room, in a white open coffin. She was wearing her Pocahontas nightie and she looked so pure and innocent. It was as if she had just fallen asleep, and if you leaned over and whispered in her ear she would wake up. On the mirror in her room, Joanna had left her little fingerprints, a reminder of a bright, cheeky, gorgeous little girl with her whole life in front of her.

I do not know how Pam and her husband Kenny and all the other families coped with the deaths of their children. They are a remarkable group of people who have been through unimaginable pain and suffering. I do not have praise high enough for my friend Pam. She has been through the worst possible thing that could happen to any parent and I am humbled by her courage.

I am very lucky that the Kellys and the McMahons (my mum's family) seem to be blessed with good health and relatively long lives. My grandmother died in 1991 and my grandfather died in 2000, both of them after a long fight with cancer. They were in a lot of pain and in a way it was a merciful release for them, but even under those circumstances, when you tell yourself that it is all for the best, death is very hard to come to terms with.

Many experts have tried to rationalise grief and to make it all neat and tidy and divided into different 'stages':

Denial – This cannot possibly be happening to me?

Anger – Why the hell is this happening to me.

Bargaining – I will be a better person if you bring them back.

Depression – I don't care about anything anymore.

Acceptance – I will learn to live with this.

While this may be helpful, it doesn't really take into account the sheer raw pain of loss, but you may well go through some or all of the above.

Acceptance is the toughest one of the lot and again there are no set rules. Some people will never be able to come to terms with losing someone they love, and it will blight their lives for ever. Others, especially if death happens when a person is very old and in great pain, will find the acceptance of that particular loss comes much easier to them.

As with every important and tough event in your life, you *must* talk about your feelings if you have lost someone you love. Bottling everything up inside does you no good what-soever. It is all right to cry and to rage and to feel that life is unfair, because sometimes it *is* bloody unfair. Many people find strength and comfort from spending time with people who are in the same situation. I know that all the parents from Dunblane who shared the common experience of hav-ing their children cold-bloodedly murdered found a lot of comfort and strength from meeting up with each other and talking.

As I have said, in June 2000 I had a miscarriage, which is another kind of bereavement. I mourned for what might have been rather than what I had. I was really helped by the women who had also suffered and who generously and kindly wrote to me, sharing their experiences. Again, you have to talk about what has happened to you. Keeping it all tight inside does you no good.

Often husbands and partners are neglected in this kind of situation and we must remember that they are grieving too.

As adults we find it tough enough trying to talk about death, so what do you tell a child who has lost a mother, father, sister or brother? How do you help them?

TELLING THE CHILDREN

The charity Winston's Wish was set up to help kids come to terms with grief and they do some terrific work trying to make it easier for children to cope with bereavement. The charity was founded by Julie Stokes who worked in a hospice in Gloucestershire and saw first-hand the need for special support for the children of terminally ill parents. These youngsters really are the 'forgotten mourners'.

Julie was helping a patient who had two children and a new baby. She had terminal cancer and was close to death. Her eldest was a bright boy of around eleven, and everyone assumed he knew what was going to happen to his mum, but Julie actually asked him whether he knew that his mum was very sick and that she wasn't going to get any better. The little boy looked at her in panic. He had no idea that his mother was going to die.

Julie knew then that something had to be done specifically to help children.

There is an understandable desire on the part of adults to protect children from bad news. We don't want to upset them more than we need to, but it is clear that we do have to be truthful. One child was having nightmares after her father died of a heart attack. Not only was she devastated at losing her daddy, but the poor little soul thought that a heart 'attack' meant that he had been stabbed. No one had thought to explain to her what it actually meant, and she was terrified that someone was going to come and attack her as well.

Children's perceptions and the gaps in their knowledge can mean that they don't always understand about death. If you tell a child that their mum or dad has 'gone to a better place', they really do think it is somewhere like Florida or Disneyland Paris, and that they will come back. You have to be very clear in how you break the news to them, to avoid any misunderstandings.

Giving children help and comfort is vital, but Winston's Wish also helps them to move on and learn to enjoy life again. 'Holding on whilst letting go' is how Julie describes it. They encourage children to build 'memory boxes' of the person who died, filled with photos and letters and things that were special to them. It helps children to remember and celebrate the good things about the parent or relative who has died.

Harry Potter has become a kind of role model to bereaved children. Harry may have lost his mum and dad, but he can still have friends and adventures. Although he'll never forget his mum and dad, life does goes on.

Lorraine's Lifelines

- If someone you know has suffered a bereavement don't cross the street to avoid them.
- Always be honest when telling children about the death of a parent or loved one.
- There's no timetable for grief – work through this at your own pace.
- Talk about your feelings and seek help if you need it.

LIFE SUPPORT

None of us can do everything by ourselves, and nor should we have to. It's vital to your happiness and well-being to have people to share the load.

I am a working mother and, like all mums with a job, I can only do my juggling act because of the support system around me. There are lots of people who help, and I couldn't possibly manage if they didn't. The whole carefully built house of cards would come tumbling down. Let me describe a typical day.

I am up quite early, usually around 5.30 a.m. (which is a big improvement on when I first presented on Breakfast TV and had to be out of bed at 3.30 in the morning). I have a quick shower, throw on my comfy tracksuit and head out. I am lucky enough to be driven into work and that hour-long journey is invaluable. It's when I re-read my scripts for the show, jot down some interview questions and read the morning papers. It means I get into work feeling on top of things. I have become so used to the journey in and out of work that usually I don't notice that we drive past some of the most beautiful buildings and famous landmarks of London, but on some clear bright mornings with the sun coming up, Big Ben and the Houses of Parliament and the view down the Thames are just so glorious that I want to burst out cheering.

I am a creature of habit and I always have a cup of tea and a glass of juice when I get into work, usually just in time to see Eamonn and Fiona start their part of the show at 7 a.m. I get my hair and make-up done by either Simon or David Jay (they are twins and the most soothing people to have around). Because of them, I don't have to worry about how I'll look, but I do notice that as the years go by it takes them just a little bit longer to do their miracle working.

As I sit in the make-up chair I get on with thinking about the interviews I'll be doing, then I always like to meet everyone I'll be talking to before we go on air, especially if they haven't done any TV before.

I have a meeting with Lisa or Sophie, who produce the show, and we go through everything in detail. We can't rehearse because the studio is being used from 6 a.m. by Penny and John and then up to 8.30 by Eamonn and Fiona, but we have all been doing it for so long that we usually get it just about right. However, it is live TV and anything can happen. This means that very often the show we plan is changed at the last minute. We've had guests delayed by traffic, and satellite links that have gone down, and breaking news stories happening while we are on air. The format of the show means that we can change things very easily, and hopefully you will never know.

When I come off air, we all have a chat about the show and then it is straight on to planning the next one, and I can change back into my comfy clothes and take off my make-up.

I then have a good chat with Gay Phillips who is my right-hand woman and who keeps me on track. Gay deals with all the letters and requests from charities and organisations that come into GMTV for all of us. I usually also have a chat with Nikki Johnceline who is our press officer and who deals with any requests for interviews and quotes.

My work is very informal, and it is a democracy – anyone in my team can put forward an idea and get a fair hearing, but that's because our producer Ros Kennedy has created the kind of atmosphere where no one feels scared or embarrassed to put forward even the most outrageous ideas.

As I have said, I try to keep on top of the letters that come in, otherwise you can get snowed under, but Gay helps me deal with all kinds of requests, from donating items to be auctioned off for charity, to more information on items we have covered in the show.

I usually have some writing to do, but I tend to do that from home.

So, as you can see, I have a big support system at work. They all really help me to do my job properly, and also to enjoy it.

At home, Steve does more than his fair share around the house. He will go shopping (and come back with the right things), and he is a far better cook than I will ever be. If I have to work late, he'll

make Rosie's tea, help her with her homework and put her to bed.

I also have Helen who takes Rosie to school for us and looks after her if Steve and I have to work late. She is a treasure and Rosie loves her. It is very comforting to know that you have someone reliable looking after your child, someone who genuinely cares for her too.

As well as Steve and Helen, there's a whole network of 'mums' from school who are always happy to help out, and we share having our children's friends home for tea or for sleepovers.

Of course there are times when it can all go wrong.

When Rosie was in nursery school, she was chosen to be Mary in the school nativity play. The best I ever managed was third shepherd from the right with my mum's tea towel draped around my head at a jaunty angle, so I was beside myself with motherly pride.

Unfortunately, it was at the time when I did a live radio show and it clashed with the one and only performance of the nativity play. I had to fight tooth and nail to get out of doing the show for one day and, although the bosses weren't happy, they relented in the end.

The show was a triumph: the shepherds forgot their words, the angels waved to their mums and Mary held baby Jesus upside down. I would never have forgiven myself if I hadn't been able to go, but I still sat there feeling guilty about taking the day off. I have come to the conclusion that guilt and being a working mum go hand in hand, and you just have to reconcile yourself to that.

I am also lucky enough to have my best friend from school living about ten minutes away from me. I have known Joyce Woodrow since secondary school and she is the pal that you can phone at three in the morning and you know she won't mind. I really think you can never overestimate the importance of friendship, especially with someone you have known for so long. It's all about being able to relax totally, be yourself, and be able to talk about absolutely anything. It is also essential to have a really good laugh.

So, from Nasir who picks me up in the morning and takes me to work, to Brenda who gives me a cuppa, to Helen who helps with Rosie, to Joyce who keeps me sane and Steve who keeps my feet on the ground, I have a fantastic life-support system, and I couldn't function properly without them all.

I also think every woman should be entitled by law to a gay male best friend, like Grace has her Will.

I love spending time with my gay friends, and when I first came to London, my pal Alan took me under his wing and was my 'walker' if I ever needed to go out on the town.

Apart from being far better dressed and much more well groomed than I could ever hope to be, he wouldn't just say 'You look great'. He would stand back and take in the effort that had been put into making everything match. He would make sure I didn't look scruffy or overdone. If one of my Wonderbra straps was higher than the other, he would fix it without one thing leading to another.

With a gay male friend you can go to the movies, have a good old bitch about the leading man, and then you are put into a taxi with no undignified scuffle.

My New Year's resolution every year (along with usual old chestnuts about getting less fat and more fit) is to spend more time with people I like. I know that might sound ridiculously obvious, but often we are so busy running to stay still that we lose touch with friends whose company we really enjoy, and we don't see as much as we should of our family members who mean a lot to us. It is crazy really, but sometimes we get too wrapped up with work or the children, or just keeping on top of things like housework and shopping. It doesn't take much of an effort to keep in touch – it doesn't have to be going out somewhere special – a quick cup of coffee, a phone call or even an e-mail lets your friends and family know you are thinking of them.

Sometimes, of course, we have to spend time with people that we find intensely irritating, or extremely negative. We all know the kind of oxygen stealers who suck the life from you, whether it's at work or it's a so-called friend or obnoxious relative. Console yourself with the thought that you wouldn't want to be them – and if you do have to see them socially, always try and dilute them with people who make you laugh.

SO WHERE DO WE GO FROM HERE?

I think we have established that having it all isn't possible. Life is not like an advert for posh perfume – we don't waft through the days swathed in pure white crinkle-free silk with not a hair out of place and flawless skin, in a world where no one farts and the ironing basket is forever empty. However, we can certainly make the most of what we have, and make a brave attempt to change what we don't like about our lives.

It's not about money – some of the most unhappy people I have ever met in my entire life are rich. Of course being able to be miserable in comfort is a luxury, but having a lot of dosh doesn't necessarily equal happiness.

Do remember that not everyone out there is having a better time than you. Just because you feel a bit miserable and you see someone younger/thinner/richer and more beautiful, don't think she is all that much happier than you. We all have much the same woes, fears and worries, and we are all trying to bumble through life as best we can.

'A problem shared is a problem halved' is one of those clichés – but just because it is a cliché doesn't mean that it isn't true. Talk over your fears, hopes, desires, anxieties and your joys with those close to you. It's good for your mental health and it helps to put everything in perspective.

Seize the day

My granny was a firm believer in *never* saving *anything* 'for best'. If you bought her some perfume, she would spray it all over herself just to put the bins out. She would never put anything to the back of the drawer or the wardrobe, saying she'd keep it for a special occasion. Posh satin nighties were worn until they fell to bits, and she squeezed her substantial size 22 bottom into silky underwear. To her, every day was special, so she would put on her best shoes and coat and pile her hair up and strut off down to the shops to get a loaf.

She always said life is not a rehearsal, and was all for seeing the bright side and making the most of the short time we have, as long as you don't hurt anyone and you try to live your life in a good and decent way. Never ever get to the end of your life and be left mourning over a lot of 'what ifs', she would say.

She was right – and remember, no one lies on their deathbed lamenting that they didn't spend enough time at the office.

Your family, your friends and yourself are the most important things – but don't put yourself at the bottom of the list *every* single time. Put on your best knickers, spray yourself with perfume, put a smile on your face, a song in your heart and get out there and start living!

real life

WHERE TO GET MORE HELP

solutions

DAWN BRESLIN

Dawn is the UK's leading confidence coach. As a single mother
she leads a busy life as managing director of Dawn Breslin Ltd, a
company that delivers life-changing 'Zest of Life' workshops for
women. She is the founder of the Dawn Breslin Teacher Training
Academy and is an adviser on *Here's Health* magazine. As well as
featuring in many articles in national newspapers, Dawn appears
regularly on national TV in the UK and the Republic of Ireland.
Website: www.dawnbreslin.com

EATING DISORDERS

Eating Disorders Association
Telephone: 0845 634 1414 (adults), 0845 634 7650 (under eighteens)

BEREAVEMENT

CRUSE Bereavement Care
Telephone: 0870 167 1677
E-mail: helpline@crusebereavementcare.org.uk
Young people between the ages of 12 and 18 call Freephone 0808 808 1677

WINSTON'S WISH

Telephone: 01452 394 377
Website: www.winstonswish.org.uk
E-mail: info@winstonswish.org.uk

BULLYING

Website: BullyingOnline – advice on bullying in school and in the workplace

Kidscape – keeping children safe from harm and abuse
2 Grosvenor Gardens
London
Telephone: 0207 730 3300

Childline
Telephone: 0800 1111

DOMESTIC VIOLENCE

National Domestic Violence Helpline
Telephone: 0207 421 0340

Women's Aid
Telephone: 08457 023 468

Refuge
Telephone: 0870 599 5443

RELATIONSHIPS

RELATE
Telephone: 01788 57 3241, 0870 601 2121

DEPRESSION

SANE – the mental health charity
Telephone: 0845 767 8000

REAL LIFE SOLUTIONS